FRACTURE AND FAILURE:

ANALYSES,
MECHANISMS
AND APPLICATIONS

FRACTURE AND FAILURE:

ANALYSES, MECHANISMS AND APPLICATIONS

Proceedings of the
American Society for Metals
Fracture and Failure Sessions

at the

1980 Western Metal and Tool Exposition and Conference
(WESTEC)

17-20 March 1980
Los Angeles, California

Edited by

Paul P. Tung
Suphal P. Agrawal
Arun Kumar
Michael Katcher

MATERIALS/METALWORKING TECHNOLOGY SERIES

American Society for Metals
Metals Park, Ohio 44073

Library of Congress Catalog Card No.: 81-66629
ISBN: 0-87170-113-8

PRINTED IN THE UNITED STATES OF AMERICA

PREFACE

This publication contains the proceedings of a symposium on the subject of fracture and failure analysis, held in conjunction with the 1980 Western Metal and Tool Exposition and Conference (WESTEC) under the asupices of the American Society for Metals and the Society of Manufacturing Engineers. In four individual sessions, the role of fracture mechanics in aerospace component design, basic mechanisms of fracture, advanced analytical techniques, and the application of this knowledge to resolve manufacturing problems were discussed. Although it has not been possible to include all of the papers presented during these sessions, we feel that those included adequately capture the basic theme of the symposium.

The series of papers in the fracture mechanics application session provide an overview of how the principles of fracture mechanics are applied in spacecraft design and fracture control, in crack growth analysis in aircraft structures, and in understanding crack initiation and early growth. The last paper emphasizes advanced nondestructive techniques used to monitor accumulated fatigue damage.

Papers in the fracture mechanisms session focus on the interrelationships between microstructures of ultra high strength steels and Ni-base alloy systems, and the mechanical properties such as strength, toughness, fatigue resistance, and stress-rupture limits of these alloys. Modern analytical tools such as transmission and scanning electron microscopes were used in these analyses.

Papers in the failure analysis sessions address both the advanced techniques used in analyzing failures and a number of actual case studies of aerospace components. Beachem correlates the fracture features to material properties, the type of failure, and the direction of crack growth. The importance of cracking direction is to isolate the origin of failure and subsequently the cause. The paper by Cox and Moller describes a methodical way to carry out failure analysis investigations and the use of a "failure analysis kit." Three subsequent papers describe case histories of failure analysis by giving specific examples of failure: a steel pot used for melting magnesium alloys, metallurgical failures in electronics industry, and the failure of silica phenolic nozzle liners from a rocket/ramjet engine.

Fracture mechanics principles and failure analysis techniques are integral parts of methods used in aerospace design, testing, and maintenance to insure the efficiency and integrity of the structures and components, and to minimize the recurrence of failures, should they unfortunately happen. This volume serves to bring these two areas together in the hope that their interrelationship is widely recognized and their usage extended beyond the realm of aerospace applications.

We take this opportunity to acknowledge gratitude to the authors, the WESTEC 1980 program committee headed by Dr. Jack R. Lewis, and the ASM office of Conferences and Expositions.

Los Angeles, California
January 1981

Paul P. Tung
Jet Propulsion Laboratory
4800 Oak Grove Drive
Pasadena, California   91109

Suphal P. Agrawal
Northrop Corporation
3901 West Broadway
Hawthorne, California   90250

Arun Kumar
Scanning Electron Analysis
Laboratories, Inc.
5301 Beethoven Street
Los Angeles, California   90066

Michael Katcher
The Marquardt Company
16555 Saticoy Street
Van Nuys, California   91409

CONTENTS

FRACTURE MECHANICS APPLICATIONS

FRACTURE MECHANISMS

FAILURE ANALYSIS

APPLICATION OF FRACTURE MECHANICS TO SPACECRAFT DESIGN

J.C. Lewis
TRW, Defense and Space Systems Group

INTRODUCTION

Fracture mechanics is an analytical tool that permits prediction of the structural behavior of macro cracks under stress, or more practically, the structural behavior of components that have cracks in them. Just as a designer will use continuum mechanics analysis to determine the strength of a component which is believed to be free of cracks (i.e., a continuum), this same designer should use fracture mechanics analysis to determine the residual strength of a component that could contain a reasonably large crack. The size of crack that is reasonably large varies with each material but a general definition could be the size of crack that would reduce the strength of a component to a level below the strength predicted by continuum mechanics.

Because launch vehicles for spacecraft are limited in the total weight they can boost free from earth's gravity field, spacecraft components are usually highly stressed to minimize weight. In addition, higher strength materials are desired to further reduce weight. The result is that the size of crack that would reduce a component's strength below that predicted by continuum mechanics is usually below the sensitivity of the available nondestructive testing (NDT) methods.

Any fracture mechanics approach to design of spacecraft components must answer, as a minimum, the following basic questions:

1. What is the largest initial crack that could exist undetected in the component after completion of nondestructive inspection?

2. If such a crack does exist in a given component, what are the environments (e.g., stress, chemical, thermal, etc.) encountered during service that could cause the initial crack to grow?

3. As a result of these environments, how much will the initial crack grow during the service life of the component?

4. To what size must the initial crack grow to cause failure at the service stresses?

This paper will describe some of the methods used to obtain answers to these basic questions for typical spacecraft components.

APPLICABLE SAFETY DOCUMENTS

Many future spacecraft will be launched from the National Aeronautics and Space Administration (NASA) Space Transportation System commonly called the Space Shuttle. The validity of fracture mechanics as an analytical and design tool has been recognized in NASA Handbook 1700.7, "Safety Policy and Requirements for Payloads Using the Space Transportation System (STS)" (1). This document permits the use of fracture mechanics for design of lightweight pressure vessels and requires fracture mechanics design/analysis of primary structural and support bracketry if the failure of such components would result in a catastrophic hazard to the Shuttle.

NASA's requirements for fracture mechanics design of pressure vessels are delineated in NASA Safety Standard NSS/HP-1740.1 (2). The specific requirements are too numerous to include here. In summary, all known crack propagation modes must be accounted for in the design and the burst pressure must be at least 1.5 times the maximum operating pressure if pressurized when people are nearby. A detailed description of methods for meeting these requirements for pressure vessels is given in Reference 3.

FRACTURE MECHANICS TERMS

The fracture mechanics discipline has many uniquely defined terms. The reader is referred to Reference 4 for a more basic understanding of fracture mechanics terms for thin spacecraft components. A few terms essential to understanding this monograph are defined below.

Within the discipline of fracture mechanics, cracks are treated as planar ellipses. The symbol for the crack depth (minor semi-axis) is "a" and the symbol for crack length (major axis) is "2c". Figure 1 illustrates the crack geometry for both surface cracks and embedded cracks. The ratio, a/c, is defined by Φ, the elliptic integral of the second kind. Reference 5 shows that:

$$\Phi = \sqrt{1 + 1.464(a/c)^{1.65}} \text{ for } a/c \leq 1 \tag{1}$$

Irwin has added a plastic zone correction factor which he includes in a parameter termed Q (6).

$$Q = \Phi^2 - 0.212 \ (\sigma/\sigma_{ys})^2 \tag{2}$$

where:

σ = applied average gross stress remote from the crack

σ_{ys} = 0.2% offset yield strength of the metal

With respect to crack growth, the ratio, a/Q, determines the severity of the crack. Within the normal variation of material properties, all cracks in the same material having the same value of a/Q and loaded to the same stress level will grow at the same rate.

The parameter that defines the relationship between crack size and the stress required for crack growth has been termed a stress intensity factor by

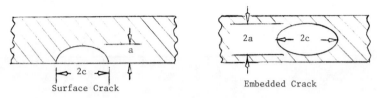

Surface Crack   Embedded Crack

Fig. 1.   Crack Geometry

Irwin and has been given the symbol, K (6). The limit value of the stress
intensity factor, i.e., that value at which the crack growth becomes uncon-
trollable, is called the fracture toughness of the material and is designated
K_{Ie} for surface cracks in tension in thin metals (7).

The subscript, I, is used to denote the pure tension or opening stress
mode. Pure shear is denoted by the subscript, II, and antiplane shear is
denoted by the subscript, III. Figure 2 shows the three crack tip displacement
modes. In spacecraft components any of these three modes may exist. Generally,
the opening mode or tension is the most severe for crack growth.

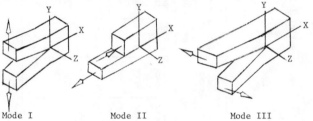

Mode I   Mode II   Mode III

Fig. 2.   Modes of Crack Surface Displacement

INITIAL CRACK SIZE

Nondestructive Testing

The answer to the first basic question will be designated $(a/Q)_i$ and is
generally obtained by some NDT method. Therefore, $(a/Q)_i$ is defined as the
largest crack that could escape detection by the most sensitive NDT method
used during acceptance testing. This does not mean that such a crack actually
does exist in each component. It means merely that a crack of this size could
exist in any given component without knowledge of its existence.

The fracture mechanics approach assumes the existence of $(a/Q)_i$ in each
component and determines the service stress/environment conditions that will
not permit $(a/Q)_i$ to grow to failure during the service life of each particular mission.

It is important to develop a sense of the limits of various NDT methods.
The example of a pressure vessel will be used. Table 1 lists the order of
magnitude of $(a/Q)_i$ for both surface cracks and embedded cracks in various
pressure vessel alloys and heat-treat conditions as a function of the NDT
method used for inspection. From Table 1, we can see that the most sensitive
method available for all cracks varies with the material selected. In heat-
treated titanium pressure vessels, a proof test in liquid nitrogen is the most
sensitive NDT method for all cracks because penetrant inspection cannot find

Table 1. Effect of Nondestructive Test Method on Measurement of Initial Crack Size[1] (Inches) for Thin-Walled Pressure Vessels

NONDESTRUCTIVE TEST METHOD / MATERIAL AND HEAT TREAT CONDITION	FLUORESCENT PENETRANT INSPECTION		PROOF TEST IN LIQUID NITROGEN		PROOF TEST AT ROOM TEMPERATURE (DIMPLING) (NOTE 2)		PROOF TEST AT ROOM TEMPERATURE (NO DIMPLING)		RADIOGRAPHY AND ULTRASONIC INSPECTION (PRESSURIZED WITH HELIUM)		RADIOGRAPHY AND ULTRASONIC INSPECTION (UNPRESSURIZED)	
	SURFACE CRACK	EMBEDDED CRACK	SURFACE CRACK	EMBEDDED CRACK	SURFACE CRACK	EMBEDDED CRACK	SURFACE CRACK	EMBEDDED CRACK	SURFACE CRACK	EMBEDDED CRACK	SURFACE CRACK	EMBEDDED CRACK
HEAT TREATED Ti-6Al-4V FORGINGS & PLATE	0.010	NOT DETECTED	0.010	0.012	0.030	0.030	0.150	0.180	0.030	0.030	0.100	0.100
ANNEALED Ti-6Al-4V PLATE & FORGINGS	0.010	NOT DETECTED	0.040	0-050	0.030	0.030	0.170	0.210	0.030	0.030	0.100	0.100
HEAT TREATED 2219 - T851 ALUMINUM FORGINGS & PLATE	0.010	NOT DETECTED	0.180	0.220	0.030	0.030	0.170	0.210	0.030	0.030	0.100	0.100

Notes: 1. Crack size is approximate.
2. Dimpling is described in the text.

embedded cracks. For aluminum alloys, radiography and ultrasonic inspection under pressure or a room temperature proof test with dimpling is the most sensitive NDT method for all cracks.

Proof Testing

Sometimes, if all conditions are right, a proof test can be used as an NDT method for determining $(a/Q)_i$. Whether a proof test screens out a meaningfully small crack is a complex function of the material, its thickness and the magnitude of the proof stress. If the proof stress is high enough and the material is the right thickness, then there will exist a size of $(a/Q)_i$ that will cause failure during the proof test. The failure mode will be either by leakage, dimpling or fracture depending on the component and the material thickness. For structural bracketry, a through-crack such as would cause leakage in a pressure vessel is not necessarily failure. If the proof stress is high enough and failure by leakage, dimpling or fracture does not occur then any crack that could exist in the component must be smaller than this determinable size.

Components other than pressure vessels can be inspected for cracks by proof testing. Maraging 350 steel shear pins for a launch vehicle spacecraft interface joint were proof tested to 339 ksi tension stress in a tensile machine to screen out any crack that could cause failure at the launch stress of 278 ksi.

For most engineering materials, the relationship between a proof stress and $(a/Q)_i$ must be determined experimentally because the relationship is not a single-valued function. The reason that the relationship is not single valued is that these materials exhibit slow, stable crack growth under the monotonically increasing stress of a proof test. The test that determines the relationship between K_{Ie} and $(a/Q)_i$ is called a crack-growth-resistance or "R-Curve" test (8) (9). An R-Curve is a plot of the applied stress intensity factor versus the instantaneous crack size (a/Q) or versus the amount of stable crack growth $\Delta(a/Q)$.

Figure 3 is an R-Curve for heat treated Ti-6Al-4V forging material containing different levels of interstitial hydrogen (10). For the high hydrogen material (115 ppm) the K_{Ie}-versus-$(a/Q)_i$ curve is single-valued. For the low hydrogen (25 ppm) and medium hydrogen (77 ppm) material the curves are not single-valued. For all three curves, however, $(a/Q)_i$ is defined as the crack size at rupture.

When extensive crack growth occurs during proof testing, one can usually find a smaller crack by radiography and ultrasonic inspection than by proof testing (Table 1). However, such radiographic and ultrasonic inspection must be performed after proof testing.

If $(a/Q)_i$ is smaller than the material thickness, then the component will fracture if a crack larger than $(a/Q)_i$ exists in the component during the proof test. If $(a/Q)_i$ is greater than the material thickness, then a crack larger than $(a/Q)_i$ will either break through the thickness and leak or the component surface will physically deform inward toward the crack tip. This deformation phenomenon is called dimpling (Figure 4) (11). Dimpling occurs when the plastic zone at the tip of the crack approaches the surface at a high value of stress intensity factor. Whether a given crack leaks or dimples is determined by the crack size and proof stress level at the crack. Deep cracks under low stress tend to leak. Shallower cracks under high stress tend to dimple. It is obvious that either leakage or dimpling can be used to establish the limits of $(a/Q)_i$ because the dimples will be found by visual inspection after the proof test.

If a statistically meaningful value of $(a/Q)_i$ is desired, then the value selected for $(a/Q)_i$ should be the upper statistical value, i.e., $(a/Q)_i$ should be the largest statistical crack that can escape detection.

ENVIRONMENTS CAUSING CRACK GROWTH

Stress Environments

Stresses are defined by their source, state and duration. Sources of stress in a pressure vessel include stresses applied by internal and external pressure, residual stresses, thermal stresses and stresses caused by launch accelerations. All potential sources of stress during the service life of the component should be identified and included in the fracture mechanics analyses. Residual stresses due to welding or forming are of particular importance because these stresses are often overlooked and can actually be higher than the stresses applied by pressure. Also, residual stresses often add directly to the applied pressure stresses.

States of stress of interest are those states that cause opening of the crack surfaces, i.e., those states that produce tensile stress components perpendicular to the crack surfaces. Such stress states are tension, shear and bending. Compression stresses are of lesser importance although they can accelerate cyclic stress crack growth rates. The summation of all tensile stresses acting perpendicular to the crack surfaces must be used in the fracture mechanics analysis.

With respect to duration, stresses are either cyclic stresses or sustained stresses. The duration of a sustained stress is relative to the chemical environment. Basically sustained stresses are long enough for interactions between the alloy and its environment. Typically, sustained stresses are longer than five seconds.

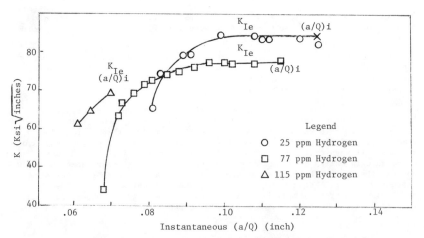

Fig. 3.   R-Curve for Ti-6Al-4V (STA) Forging Material

Cyclic stresses are important for two different reasons. Any cyclic stress causes some amount of growth of $(a/Q)_i$. In addition, cyclic stresses potentially can create cracks during service at geometric notches and points of residual stress. Proper pressure vessel design accounts for both conditions. Classical cumulative fatigue damage relationships must not be ignored in favor of cyclic stress crack propagation analyses.

Classical Chemically Induced Failures

Some chemical environments can cause failure without a pre-existing crack. These are the environments associated with classical corrosion, classical stress corrosion cracking and the classical metallurgical embrittlement mechanisms such as hydrogen embrittlement, liquid-metal embrittlement, radiation embrittlement, oxidation embrittlement, nitrogen embrittlement, etc. For any given aerospace pressure vessel material, exposure to any known corrosive, stress corrosive or embrittling environment must be avoided. Fracture mechanics methods should not be used to design a pressure vessel to contain such environments.

Chemical Environments Causing Crack Growth

Even though a given chemical does not generate a crack in a given alloy nor contribute to an embrittling mechanism, the chemical has the potential for causing growth of pre-existing cracks. A good example is isopropyl alcohol and heat treated Ti-6Al-4V forgings (12). Although no crack generation nor embrittling mechanism is known for this alloy in this environment, under sustained stresses pre-existing cracks in this alloy grow in isopropyl alcohol at room temperature at about fifty percent of K_{Ie}. Until properly generated experimental data exist which indicate no susceptibility, any chemical environment, including inert gases, must be considered potential environments for crack growth. For example, under exposure to high-purity helium, cracks in heat-treated Ti-6Al-4V forgings grow under sustained stress at about eighty percent of K_{Ie} (13). ASTM Committee E-24 on Fracture Mechanics Test Methods has started work on standardizing testing of sustained load crack growth in inert environments.

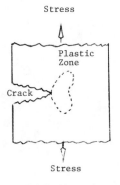

Thick Material

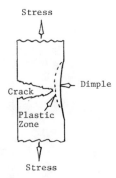

Thin Material

Fig. 4. Dimpling Phenomenon

Chemical environments can affect the threshold stress intensity factor above which crack growth will occur under sustained load and also, the cyclic load crack growth rate. Some chemicals affect both, some affect only one and some affect neither.

Thermal Environments

Thermal environments can affect crack growth in several different ways. They can cause metallurgical embrittlement such as temper embrittlement. They can sensitize an alloy to corrosion, e.g., sensitized stainless steel. They can change either the sustained stress crack growth rate or the cyclic stress crack growth rate or both for any given chemical environment, e.g., nitrogen tetroxide with titanium. Thermal environments can also cause thermal stresses that add directly to the other applied stresses.

CRACK GROWTH DURING SERVICE

Cyclic Stress Crack Growth Rates

Cyclic stress crack growth rates (da/dN) must be determined for each environment in which the component stress will be cycled. For an actual mission, this usually means testing in the propellant for pressure vessels and at least one inert environment such as helium, air or vacuum for other components. Inert environment da/dN rates are also needed for embedded cracks which are not exposed to internal environments. Tests at several different cyclic stress frequencies are needed because da/dN is often a strong function of frequency for non-inert environments.

Many propellants, e.g., nitrogen tetroxide and hydrazine have da/dN rates identical to those for air. Figure 5 is a curve of da/dN versus the cyclic stress intensity factor, ΔK, for heat-treated Ti-6Al-4V plate in air at 70°F taken from Reference 14.

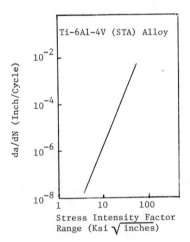

Fig. 5. Cyclic Stress Crack
Growth Rate Data

Sustained Stress Crack Growth Threshold

Under sustained stress for most environments, there exists a threshold stress intensity factor below which crack growth will not occur (4). As long as the applied stress intensity factors in the component are less than this threshold stress intensity factor (designated K_{th}), any cracks in the component will not grow under sustained stress, no matter how long the sustained stress duration. Figure 6 is a typical sustained stress crack growth threshold curve for aged Ti-6Al-4V forgings and unaged welds and unaged heat affected zones where the initial applied stress intensity factor, K_{Ii} is normalized by the fracture toughness, K_{Ie}. The value of K_{Ii} below which crack growth does not occur for any duration is denoted K_{th} (4). The crack growth rate above K_{th} has far too much scatter to attempt to design to a finite rate. Therefore, K_{th} is usually taken as the design limit.

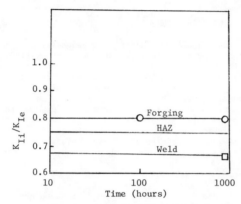

Fig. 6. Sustained Load Crack Growth Threshold for Ti-6Al-4V (STA) Alloy in Refined Hydrazine at 40-44°C

CRITICAL CRACK SIZE

Since K_{th} is chosen as the limit design condition for most missions, the value of crack size, $(a/Q)_{th}$ that will cause any applied stress intensity factor to exceed K_{th} becomes the critical crack size for the component under sustained stress. If no sustained stress is applied to the component during the mission then the crack size that will cause the cyclic stress to result in an applied stress intensity factor that equals the fracture toughness will be the critical crack size. This critical crack size is designated $(a/Q)_{CR}$. The difference between $(a/Q)_i$ and $(a/Q)_{CR}$ is the amount of cyclic stress crack growth that can be tolerated in a component without failure.

ANALYSIS

Once $(a/Q)_i$ and $(a/Q)_{CR}$ are determined for a given component, the total amount of cyclic stress crack growth, $\Delta(a/Q)_i$ is determined by summing the product of the number of stress cycles and da/dN. Reference 15 is a good review of cyclic crack growth rate calculations.

$$\Delta(a/Q)_i = \Sigma \ BN(da_n/dN) \tag{3}$$

where:

$\Delta(a/Q)_i$ = total increase in the initial crack size resulting from cyclic stress in units of m (IN)

B = multiplying constant for total number of stress cycles (usually ≥ 4.0)

N = total number of stress cycles during a mission

da_n/dN = instantaneous crack growth rate for the nth stress cycle in units of m (IN)

The final design condition is that $(a/Q)_i + \Delta(a/Q)_i < (a/Q)_{CR}$.

STRESS INTENSITY FACTOR SOLUTIONS

Stress intensity factor solutions differ with geometry and stress field. Often, specific solutions for the actual geometry and stress field being analyzed will not exist in the literature. Considerable cost can often be avoided by assuming a geometry and stress field that is known to produce a worse effect than the actual conditions but for which a stress intensity factor solution exists. If this worse-case approach still shows positive margin then no further effort is needed. Sometimes, however, conditions of weight and reliability will require generation of a specific stress intensity factor solution. References 16-18 are compilations of stress intensity factor solutions and also describe how to generate a stress intensity factor solution.

NUMBER OF STRESS CYCLES

The number of stress cycles can differ greatly between components on the same spacecraft. Pressure vessels undergo high cyclic stresses during cyclic pressurizations and launch vibration whereas most other components are highly stressed only during launch vibration. For components whose mass is small compared to the mass of the spacecraft, the total number of cycles is taken as the resonant frequency times the duration. The proportion of these cycles at a given stress level is obtained from the Rayleigh distribution (19). For components whose mass is large compared to the mass of the spacecraft, the number of cycles at a given stress level is considerably less but requires a complex response analysis to determine. Again, a worse-case analysis where resonance is assumed for these large components can save costs if positive margin can still be shown at resonance.

DESIGN DATA TESTING

Determination of the conditions for crack growth during proof testing and also the conditions for dimpling is accomplished during a single R-curve test. Reference 9 describes how to generate R-curves in general. However, some specific additional procedures are needed to determine crack growth and dimpling for surface cracks.

Pre-cracked tensile specimens are fabricated to the same thickness and of the same material as the area of interest of the component. The need to test similar thicknesses as the component derives from the R-curve behavior of materials and is also a specific requirement of Reference 2 for thin-walled pressure vessels. Figure 7 shows a typical specimen configuration.

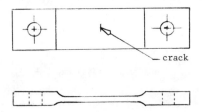

Fig. 7. Typical Surface-Crack Tensile Specimen

Clips are attached to the specimen on either side of the crack faces. A clip gage is then used to plot clip-gage opening as the load is varied (Figure 8). A load is applied monotonically to the specimen until the load-versus-clip-gage-opening curve (compliance curve) becomes nonlinear. From this point on, periodic instantaneous slopes are taken by dropping the load a small amount. These instantaneous slopes are necessary to separate plastic-zone hinging from crack growth. Figure 9 is a compliance curve for 0.25 inch thick heat treated Ti-6Al-4V forging material. Dimpling is determined by visually inspecting the back face at each new slope point.

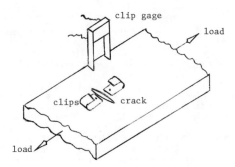

Fig. 8. Clip Gage Attachment Method

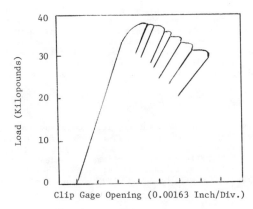

Fig. 9. Typical Compliance Curve

Ehret has derived the relationship between clip-gage opening and crack depth for titanium alloys (20). This relationship is:

$$\frac{COD}{P} = \left(\frac{G}{Etw}\right) \exp\left[16.5\ (a/\phi^2)\ \exp\left(\frac{0.074}{t}\right)\right] \qquad (4)$$

where:

COD/P = the reciprocal of the instantaneous slope of the load-versus-clip-gage-opening curve in m/N (in/lb)

E = Young's modulus in psi

G = gage length between clip gage attachment points in inches

ϕ = elliptic integral of the second kind

a = minor semi-axis of elliptical crack (crack depth) in inches

t = specimen thickness in inches, and

w = specimen width in inches.

The effective gage length, G, is calibrated for each specimen by measuring the actual crack size (a/ϕ^2) from the fracture surface. The initial slope of the compliance curve is then measured and G is calculated from Equation 4. This value of G is then used for all subsequent crack size calculations for that particular specimen.

From the instantaneous values of a/ϕ^2 at each new slope point and the load at each point, corresponding values of K_I can be calculated. K_I is then plotted versus (a/Q) or Δ(a/Q) as in Figure 3.

Data for da/dN are obtained with precracked specimens that are cyclically stressed for a small number of cycles in the total environment of interest. The total crack growth is divided by the number of cycles and plotted against ΔK. Reference 4 describes these methods in detail.

K_{th} is determined with precracked specimens that are loaded to different values of stress intensity factors for different times. If the specimen has not broken after a predetermined time, the specimen is usually removed from testing and broken apart to determine the amount of crack growth that has occurred. Increasingly lower values of stress intensity factor are tested until that value is determined for which no growth has taken place. A test duration of 1000 hours is usually sufficient to determine the threshold. References 4, 11 and 13 describe the test method in considerable detail.

CONCLUSIONS

Fracture mechanics design/analysis has application to any spacecraft component in which a crack can cause premature failure. Specific components to which the methods have already been applied include propellant tanks, inert fluid tanks, solid rocket propellants and motor cases, structural bracketry and struts, electronic components, tubing, valves, adhesive joints and ceramic tiles. Many other applications will be found with the advent of the Shuttle launch vehicle.

REFERENCES

(1) Anonymous, "Safety Policy and Requirements for Payloads Using the Space Transportation System (STS)," NHB 1700.7, National Aeronautics and Space Administration, Washington, DC, May 1979.

(2) Anonymous, "NASA Aerospace Pressure Vessel Safety Standard," NSS/HP-1740.1, National Aeronautics and Space Administration, Washington, DC, 22 February 1974.

(3) J.C. Lewis, "Fracture Mechanics Design of Shuttle Payload Pressure Vessels," 1980 JANNAF Propulsion Meeting, Monterey, California, March 11-13, 1980.

(4) Anonymous, "Fracture Control of Metallic Pressure Vessels," SP-8040, National Aeronautics and Space Administration, Washington, DC, May 1970.

(5) J.G. Merkle, "A Review of Some of the Existing Stress Intensity Factor Solutions for Part-Through Surface Crack," ORNL-TM 3983, Oak Ridge National Laboratory, January 1973.

(6) G.P. Irwin, "Crack-Extension Force for a Part-Through Crack in a Plate," Journal of Applied Mechanics, Series E, Vol. 29, No. 4, pp. 651-654, December 1962.

(7) ASTM,"Recommended Practice for Fracture Testing with Surface-Crack Tension Specimens," ASTM E740-80, American Society for Testing and Materials, Philadelphia, PA 1980.

(8) ASTM, Fracture Toughness Evaluation by R-Curve Methods, Special Technical Publication 527, American Society for Testing and Materials, Philadelphia, Pennsylvania, 1973.

(9) ASTM, "Tentative Recommended Practice for R-Curve Determination," ANSI/ ASTM E561-78T, Annual Book of ASTM Standards, Part 10, 1979, American Society of Testing and Materials, Philadelphia, Pennsylvania, 1979.

(10) Joseph Clifton Lewis, "Effect of Hydrogen on Fracture of Titanium," Thesis for Master of Science Degree in Engineering, University of California at Los Angeles, Los Angeles, California, 1979.

(11) L.R. Toth and J.C. Lewis, "Effect of Chloride Ion Content in Unsymmetrical Dimethyl Hydrazine Propellant on Fracture Properties of Structural Alloys," AFRPL-TR-76-1, January 1976.

(12) J.C. Lewis, et al., "Fracture Mechanics Design Data for Ti-6Al-4V Titanium Alloy Tanks Containing Hydrazine," Chemical Propulsion Information Agency Publication 280, 1976 JANNAF Propulsion Meeting, Volume III, December 1976.

(13) J.C. Lewis and J.T. Kenny, "Sustained Load Crack Growth Design Data for Ti-6Al-4V Titanium Alloy Tanks Containing Hydrazine," AIAA/SAE 12th Propulsion Conference, Palo Alto, California, July 26-29, 1976 (AIAA Paper No. 76-769).

(14) Anonymous, Damage Tolerant Design Handbook, MCIC-HB-01, Metals and Ceramics Information Center, Battelle Memorial Institute, Columbus, Ohio, January 1975.

(15) J.B. Chang, ed., Part-Through Crack Fatigue Life Prediction, STP 687, American Society for Testing and Materials, Philadelphia, Pennsylvania, 1979.

(16) H. Tada, et al., <u>The Stress Analysis of Cracks Handbook</u>, Del Research Corporation, St. Louis, Missouri, 1973.

(17) George Sih, <u>Handbook of Stress Intensity Factors</u>, Lehigh University Press, Bethlehem, Pennsylvania, 1973.

(18) D.P. Rooke and D.J. Cartwright, <u>Compendium of Stress Intensity Factors</u>, Her Majesty's Stationery Office, London, England, 1976.

(19) Cyril M. Harris and Charles E. Crede, <u>Shock and Vibration Handbook</u>, Vol. 1, p. 11-11, McGraw-Hill, New York, NY, 1961.

(20) R.M. Ehret, "Part-Through-Crack Elastic Compliance Calibration," North American Rockwell Space Division, Downey, California, Internal Document No. SD71-329, October 1, 1971.

FRACTURE CONTROL APPLICATIONS ON
SPACE SHUTTLE RCS THRUSTERS

J. H. Schmidt
M. Katcher

The Marquardt Company

INTRODUCTION

It is the goal of any fracture control program to design components which will provide structural integrity even in the presence of undetected flaws. This assurance shall be maintained with minimum impact to weight and cost. The objective of this program was to establish those criteria, procedures, and controls necessary to prevent structural failures in the Space Shuttle Reaction Control Thrusters (SSRCT), due to the presence of defects and flaws that are assumed to be present in all fabricated metal components of the thrusters.

The basic assumption employed in the fracture control program was that real structures contain crack-like flaws located at the most critical area of the component, in the most unfavorable orientation.

A large effort necessary to implement the fracture control plan was required of various engineering disciplines to generate the data to perform fracture analyses and thus to complete the fracture control plan. This data basis included the following:

A. Structural definition

B. Structural environmental load definition

C. Comprehensive structural analysis that includes a fatigue analysis

D. Material properties

E. Inspection technique availability and reliability for flaw detection.

Results of the fracture control plan were supported by prototype thruster testing and then by qualification (qual) testing of actual production hardware.

These tests substantiated the findings of the analyses of the fracture control plan and revealed the usefulness of a fracture analysis in improving component survivability. It is concluded that the imposed fracture control plan proved to be one of the most restrictive criteria placed upon the design and development of the Space Shuttle Reaction Control Thrusters.

I. FRACTURE CONTROL PLAN

Effective management of the Fracture Control Plan was accomplished by the establishment of a Design Review Board for Fracture Control. Responsibility for implementation of the Fracture Control Plan and associated reviews was vested in the Program Manager and the following groups, which made up the board:

1. Engineering Structural Design

2. Engineering Structural Analysis

3. Materials Engineering

4. Quality Assurance

The Design Group was specifically instructed to implement design practices which provided components capable of proper function under adverse conditions. Items requiring attention include:

A. Stress concentration reduction

B. Elimination or reduction of residual and assembly stresses

C. Incorporation of features to preclude stress corrosion cracking

D. Compatibility of the design with manufacturing methods; and

E. Designation on appropriate drawings for inspection requirements of flaw detection, plus the responsibility of assuring that all parts

designated as "fracture critical" bear an identifying legend or general note on the drawing.

The Structural Analysis group was responsible for performance of the crack growth predictive analysis. This analysis
is performed in addition to conventional static and fatigue
analyses for each component. Because these calculations could
result in a component being designated as fracture critical,
the proper application of assumptions, analysis methods, and
initial flaw sizes used in the computations had to be assured.

The Materials Engineering group was responsible for the
implementation of documentation for materials procurement and
fabrication process control necessary to achieve and maintain
crack growth resistance characteristics while precluding detrimental effects contributing to flaw initiation. Material
properties utilized in the crack growth predictions were vali-
dated for the intended thermal and chemical environment.
Additional data necessary to complete the analyses, and not
available in the literature, was generated by test and vali-
dated by the Materials group.

The primary objectives of the Quality Assurance group
were to institute maintenance of material properties and to
develop and/or to provide the non-destructive evaluation (NDE)
techniques adequate to detect flaws that could be found with
90% probability and a confidence level of 95%. Further responsibility included a review of engineering documentation
pertinent to fracture critical components for adequacy of
crack detection methods, accessibility for inspection where
required, and methods to preserve fracture mechanics related
properties.

1A. MODIFICATIONS TO GENERAL PROCEDURES AND REQUIREMENTS

A General Fracture Control Plan logic as shown in
Figures 1a, 2a, 3, was imposed on contractors by the National
Aeronautics and Space Administration (NASA). To implement the
Fracture Control Plan efficiently several important and very
constructive changes were made to the general guidelines presented in Figures 1a, 2a, and 3. These changes led to sub-
stantial reductions in cost and time while complying with the
original intent of the plan, that is, to provide structural
integrity even in the presence of undetected flaws.

To identify a part as fracture critical increases cost
and lengthens production time. All such parts required

individual identification as fracture critical, that is, raw
stock, parts and related paperwork and drawings. The purpose
was to put responsible engineering, handling and manufacturing
organizations on alert as to the special nature of the end
items. In particular, the quality assurance department was
alerted that special crack size rejection criteria were
applicable.

Because other requirements imposed by NASA distinguished
pressure vessels for low pressure use and those for high
pressure use, all engine components under low pressure were
exempt from identification as "fracture critical". This
exemption was an allowable deviation from the Fracture
Control Plan logic as presented in FIgure 1a.

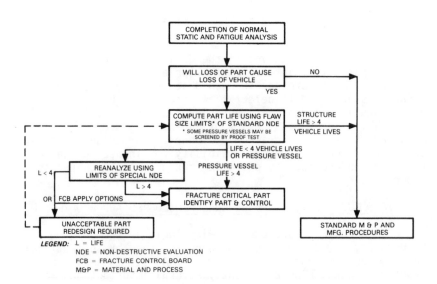

Figure 1a.   Fracture Critical Part Selection Logic

Pressure vessels per Figure 1a were defined as containers for
the storage of compressed fluids that would release more than
14,250 foot-pounds of energy and having a safety factor less
than 4.0. Since all pressure components of the SSRCT system
would release less than 14,250 foot- pounds upon exploding,

SSRCT components were not designated fracture critical. NASA felt that greater energy release could cause loss of the vehicle. Therefore, parts that had to contain pressure without leakage need not be defined as pressure vessels and were subject only to the requirements of standard airframe structure per the revised flow chart of Figure 1b.

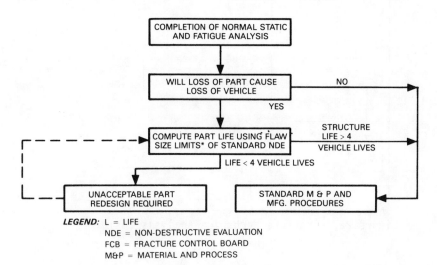

Figure 1b. Revised Fracture Critical Part Selection Logic

Several pressure retaining components of the SSRCT system had wall thickness less than 0.191 cm (0.075 in). They posed a fracture analysis problem because the Fracture Control Plan logic per Figure 2a required analysis of a through-crack (TC). Such a crack would cause a leak and violate pressure containment. Therefore, the flow chart was revised by eliminating the through-crack analysis option and allowing nly the part-through-crack (PTC) analysis option while maintaining quality through standard Nondestructive Evaluation (NDE). Crack growth predictions could then be made valid by requiring both penetrant and X-ray rather than only one inspection method. Therefore, a revised logic was created as presented in Figure 2b.

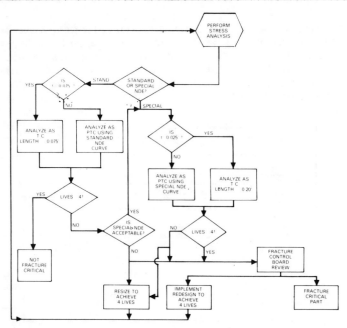

Figure 2a.   Fracture Mechanics Analysis Logic

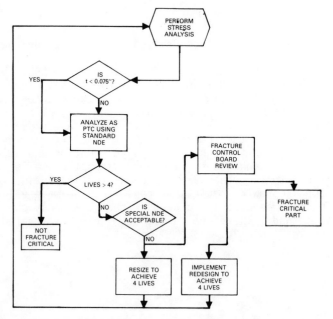

Figure 2b.   Revised Fracture Mechanics Analysis Logic

Governing requirements define the level of inspection as a function of the initial crack size. Two potential levels of inspection include standard Non Destructive Evaluation (NDE). Standard NDE dictates the use of a larger initial crack size for analysis, as compared to special NDE, because common inspection techniques such as penetrant, X-ray and ultrasonic demand larger crack size to meet the requirements of finding cracks at a 90% probability and a 95% confidence. To allow a larger number of cycles to failure, the engineering functions can choose to analyze for a smaller defect but this imposes on the quality assurance function special NDE requirements. Quality Assurance must then demonstrate to the customer that they in fact can find smaller defects with a 90% probability and a 95% confidence. It was therefore beneficial with respect to cost and schedule to avoid special NDE analysis (and therefore special NDE inspection) and pursue analysis of cracks under the jurisdiction of standard NDE. To do this, the NASA generated curves presented in Figure 3, were used as a guide for choosing initial flaw sizes for fracture analysis.

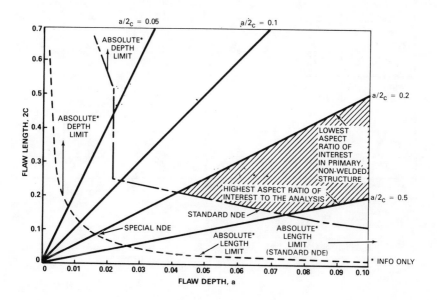

Figure 3.   NDE Detection Limits - Surface Flaws

An additional NASA requirement restricted the crack shape or aspect ratio from a/2c of 0.2 to 0.5. Thus, Marquardt was restricted to analyzing parts having initial crack sizes within the shaded area of Figure 3. Therefore, analysis of all parts assumed an initial crack length on the surface, 2c, of 0.3810 cm (0.150 in.) and, where thicknesses, w, were greater than 0.1905 cm, (0.075 in.), a crack depth, a, of 0.1905 cm (0.075 in.). Because X-ray can detect defects with 90% probability and 95% confidence, as determined by NASA, to depths of 70% of the thickness, initial crack depths of less than 0.1905 cm (0.075 in.) were allowed. When part thickness was less than 0.1905 cm (0.075 in.) and crack depths chosen also less than 0.1905 cm (0.075 in.), the requirements per Table 1 were applicable as long as both penetrant and X-ray were imposed by the drawing rather than just one method of inspection.

Table 1. Quality Assurance - Flaw Sizes

Inspection Technique	Penetrant	X-Ray	Penetrant	X-Ray	Ultra-Sonics
Thickness $t \sim$ cm. (in.)	≤ 0.1905 (0.075)	≤ 0.1905 (0.075)	> 0.1905 (0.075)	> 0.1905 (0.075)	
Type of Crack	*TC CE ED	PTC CE ED	PTC CE ED	PTC CE ED	Embedded -Cicular
Depth $a \sim$ cm. in.)	t	70% t 0.0203 (.008 min)	0.1905 (0.075) min.	70% 0.0203 (.008 min)	0.18034 (0.071)
Length $2C \sim$ cm. (in.)	0.381 (0.150)	0.381 (0.150)	0.381 (0.150)	0.381 (0.150)	0.3607 (0.142)

* TC ≆ Thru-Crack, CE ≡ Center, ED ≡ Edge,
  PTC ≆ Part-thru Crack, CO ≅ Corner

All of the changes or simplifications were done in order to eliminate both

Fracture critical designations of structural components and

Special NDE inspection requirements.

Elimination of fracture critical designations meant that a strict adherance to part identification and control from raw stock to finished item could be deleted. Special NDE requirements meant special instruction and certification of inspection personnel, and thus becomes a worthy candidate to delete. However, the deletion of these two items from the Fracture Control Plan now requires each structural component to either exceed the 4 life requirement or be redesigned.

II. STRUCTURAL DEFINITION

The structures receiving the attention of the Fracture Control Plan are the reaction control thrusters used on the Space Shuttle Orbiter. The method of controlling the Orbiter (pitch, yaw, roll) and providing its flight phase and upon reentry is performed by the Reaction Control System (RCS). This system is used for external tank separation and also serves as a backup for the Orbital Maneuvering System (OMS) for the de-orbit burn. The SSRCS contains 38 primary thrusters and 6 smaller vernier thrusters (Figure 4).

The forward fuselage of the shuttle contains the forward propulsion modules which have 14 primary and 2 vernier thrusters. These two pods are located on either side of the aft section under the vertical stabilizer. The thruster propellants are monomethylhydrazine as the fuel and nitrogen tetroxide as the oxidizer. The propellants are earth storable and are hypergolic (ignite upon contact with each other). There are several different thruster configurations, depending upon where they are located in the fuselage. These configurations are categorized as non-scarfed, short-scarfed, and long scarfed thrusters depending upon the contour of the exit nozzle.

The fracture control plan is applied, in general, to all thrusters. However, in order to limit the discussion, only the structural components of a typical non-scarf aft primary thruster was selected for further details of structural definition. A schematic of a non-scarf aft primary engine is shown in Figure 5, and illustrates most of the structural

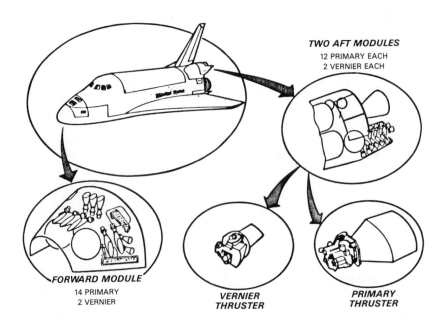

Figure 4.   Location of SSRCS on Space Shuttle

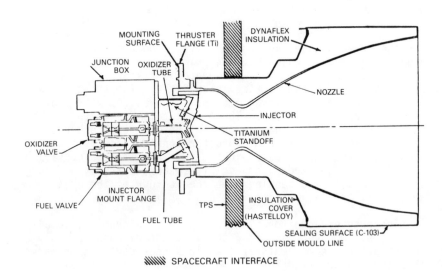

Figure 5.   Typical Non-Scarf Aft Thruster

components included in the Fracture Control Plan. Of note-
worthy importance are the following items.

o   Chamber, Nozzle

o   Injector

o   Mounting Flange

o   Oxidizer and Fuel Valves

o   Junction Box

o   Pressure Transducer (not shown)

o   Titanium Valve Standoff

o   Oxidizer Fuel and Pressure Transducer Tubes.

III. LOAD ENVIRONMENT

The SSRCS thrusters are subjected to a variety of structural loads during each Space Shuttle mission. The mission pro-
file required investigation of aerodynamic, shock, vibration,
thermal, installation, and internal pressure loads.

All of the load conditions were analyzed. However, based
upon stress magnitude and/or number of applied load cycles
only 4 load conditions were selected that could prove critical
in a fracture analysis. These 4 load conditions are discussed
below.

The random vibration was analytically found to be the
most severe of the vibratory environments considered for the
thrusters. Not only were predicted stress magnitudes higher
than all other vibratory load cases, but the number of stress
cycles approached 2 million cycles for many of the thruster
structural components. Therefore, a severe fatigue environment also resulted from the random load condition.

The thermal environment was dominated by two cases:
re-entry heat and engine firing in cold space. Engine firing
in cold space produces nozzle and insulation cover stresses
that are well above tensile yield. However, by using the
rationale that survival of the vehicle did not depend upon the
loss of these structural components, both of these structural
items were eliminated from the fracture analysis.

Installation loads, such as bolt or torque loads, were considered, only if the summation of stresses was tensile. Fracture mechanics cannot handle compressive loads mathematically, even though adjustments for their presence can be and were considered in the analysis.

Pressure loads and resulting structural component stresses were dominant in fracture analysis considerations due to the large off operation pressures imposed, preignition explosions called spikes, and the large number of cycles seen in every 100 missions. (1 life- 100 missions).

Typical pressures used were:

Operation	=	250 psi (1724 Mpa)
Proof	=	3000 psi (20,683 Mpa)
Spike	=	10,000 psi (68,943 Mpa)

IV. ANALYTICAL TOOLS

Included within and supported by the Fracture Control Plan were the following analytical programs which were used to compute all expected stresses and to predict crack growth for the load environments. These programs were:

1. STARDYNE, which is a general purpose finite element structural computer program that was used for all vibration (fatigue) and thermal environments. The entire thruster was structurally characterized via the use of this finite element program.

2. SAAS, which is a limited finite element structural program used only for detailed axisymetric static (pressure, thermal) stress analyses and for the generation of stiffness matrices that were incorporated into STARDYNE.

3. FLAGRO, which is a computer program developed by Rockwell International, Space Shuttle Group (RI/SSG) was the basis for the fracture analysis portion of the Fracture Control Plan.

The FLAGRO program utilizes the Ejret-Collipriest equation:

$$\frac{da}{dN} = C(K_c \Delta K_o)^{n/2} \; EXP. \left[\ln (K_c / \Delta K_o)^{n/2} \; ARCTANH \left\{ \frac{\ln \left[K^2 / (1-R) K_c \Delta K_o \right]}{\ln \left[(1-R) K_c / \Delta K_o \right]} \right\} \right]$$

which is integrated for the cyclic load environment to obtain flaw growth per unit load cycle. Definitions of the terms used in the above equation are as follows:

C = Crack growth rate equation coefficient
n = Crack growth rate equation exponent
K_c = Stress Intensity for fracture
ΔK_o = Threshold stress intensity range

R = Load range (minimum load)/(maximum load)

ΔK = Cyclic stress intensity range.

V. INSPECTION TECHNIQUES AND ASSUMED CRACK SIZES

The flaw detection capabilities of any given NDE technique are, at best, difficult to define precisely. The present trend is to apply statistical methods which demonstrate the validity of critical flaw-detection capabilities. Samples with known flaws (artificially grown fatigue cracks) of various sizes are inspected; then statistical analysis of the detection results is made to determine the crack size range for which 90% probability of detection at a 95% confidence level can be demonstrated.

At The Marquardt Company (TMC) a table of inspection technique versus crack size (length and depth) was created from data supplied by RI/SSG and by NASA. Table 1 presents a summary of these efforts and is based upon the following:

a. All crack sizes per technique are the minimum sizes that can be found with 90% probability and a confidence level of 95%.

b. The crack sizes shown require no special training nor special certification of personnel to achieve the aforementioned probability of detection and confidence level.

The creation of Table 1 allowed the following simplifications to be implemented into the fracture analysis portion of the Fracture Control Plan.

1. The table provides a correlation between flaw size and inspection technique.

2. Via the use of penetrant and X-ray all part thicknesses are now considered Standard NDE.

3. All flaw sizes of Table 1 are to be considered maximum for Standard NDE flaw size analytical assumptions.

4. Table 1 establishes unique Standard NDE flaw sizes and thus unique a/2c as compared to an analytical approach that must assume various a/2c ratios as shown in Figure 3 for the Standard NDE curve.

VI. THRUSTER MATERIALS

The materials selected for the hardware development of the Reaction Control Thruster are varied, but most are typical of present day space applications. Table 2 lists all the materials included in the fracture analysis, and thus subject to the Fracture Control Plan. All of the material constants necessary for a fracture analyses (Table 2) were obtained from Reference 1 and Reference 2, however, the data for Cb-103 was generated at the Rockwell International Space System Group (RI/SSG) with compact tension test coupons supplied by TMC.

The last column of Table 2 presents a relative measure of crack growth/load cycle derived from the Paris Equation shown in the footnote of Table 2. These values offer a comparison between materials for crack growth rate sensitivity and illustrate the extreme sensitivity of Titanium to flaws as compared to other materials used on the thrusters.

Table 2. Typical Required Material Properties for Fracture Analysis

MATERIAL	K_{PTC} ~ MPa√cm (K_{SI} √in)	ΔK_0 ~ MPa√cm (K_{SI} √in)	c ~ cm/(CYCLE (MPa√cm)^n) in/(CYCLE (K_{SI} √in)^n)	n —	K_{TH} ~ MPa√cm (K_{SI} √in)	K_c ~ MPa√cm (K_{SI} √in)	*da/dN cm/CYCLE (in/CYCLE)
INCO-718	1263.85 (115)	164.85 (15)	1.571×10^{-6} (4.0×10^{-4})	27	—	1263.85 (115)	57.28 (22.55)
E-BRITE	549.5 (50)	109.9 (10)	1.091×10^{-6} (5.7×10^{-4})	3.0	—	549.5 (50)	22.63 (8.91)
E-BRITE WELDS	439.6 (40)	109.9 (10)	1.091×10^{-6} (5.7×10^{-4})	3.0	—	439.6 (40)	11.58 (4.56)
TITANIUM 6AL-4VI	879.2 (80)	65.94 (6)	69.804×10^{-6} (5.67×10^{-4})	3.184	—	879.2 (80)	181.71 (71.54)
TITANIUM 6AL-4VI EB WELDS	549.5 (50)	131.88 (12)	2.292×10^{-6} (1.35×10^{-3})	3.05	—	549.5 (50)	62.94 (24.78)
TITANIUM 3AL-2.5VI	549.5 (50)	38.465 (3.5)	93.227×10^{-6} (1.0×10^{-3})	3.3	549.5 (50)	549.5 (50)	104.24 (41.04)
Cb-103	879.2 (80)	131.88 (12)	361.567×10^{-6} ($1/6 \times 10^{-2}$)	1.97	879.2 (80)	879.2 (80)	58.22 (22.92)
AM 355	1044.05 (95)	109.9 (10)	275.78×10^{-6} (1.25×10^{-2})	1.98	1044.05 (95)	1044.05 (95)	66.32 (26.11)

* da/dN = C(ΔK)^n; R = 0
  ΔK = 0.5 K_c

VII. RESULTS

The results from implementation of the Fracture Control Plan to the development of the Reaction Control Thrusters are, in general, as follows:

1. All thruster structural components, but the thruster nozzles and seal surfaces, were considered critical to the mission and thus included for fracture analysis and subject to the results of the analysis.

2. No structural components of the thrusters were considered to fall within the category of pressure vessels.

3. All thruster structural components and, in particular, weld joints have been stress analyzed and have been included in the fracture analysis.

4. All thruster structural components pass the
    following fracture control requirements

    Standard NDE flaw size assumptions
    per Table 1 and

    No through-crack nor instability at
    less than 400 missions (4 lives of
    the load environment.

5. All drawings reflect the inspection requirements
    of Table 1.

6. No structural components required

    A fracture critical designation, nor

    Special NDE level of inspection.

All the above results were achieved by either sufficiently low stress levels or part redesign.

Discussions of the detailed results in this paper is
limited to one structural component which provided the most
challenge during the thruster development. The structural
component under consideration is the Titanium (6A1-4V)standoff
shown in Figure 5 and further detailed in Figure 6. Two cases
of the titanium standoff are considered; the original
design prior to standoff failure, and the redesign after a
structural mockup failed fatigue test. A structural mockup
of the standoff made according to the original design failed
during fatigue testing by developing a crack in an electron
beam weld near an access hole required to permit passage of
the fuel tube from the fuel valve to the injector. The test
verified results exhibited by the FLAGRO analysis of the
original design which showed that it was inadequate to sur-
vive mission requirements.

Initially, the margin of safety analysis was performed
using the stress results from a STARDYNE finite element
computer program. Table 3 presents a summary of the critical
load environment and the stress margin of safety for each
case. The titanium material allowables used for margins are
also presented in Table 3. Review of the results of Table 3
show that, for either case, all large positive margins exist
and would not indicate that either case was failure sensitive.

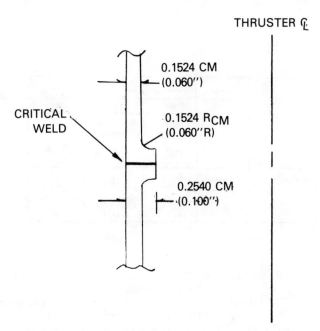

THRUSTER ₵

0.1524 CM
(0.060'')

CRITICAL
WELD

0.1524 R_CM
(0.060''R)

0.2540 CM
(0.100'')

Figure 6.   Standoff Detail

Table 3.   Stress Analyses Results

EXAMPLE NUMBER	MATERIAL	LOAD CASE	STRESS [2] MPa (KSI)	NUMBER [3] OF CYCLES	M.S. [4] YIELD F.S. = 1.0	M.S. ULTIMATE F.S. = 1.4	M.S. FATIGUE	THICKNESS CM. (IN.)
1	TITANIUM [1] 6AL-4V E.B. WELD	RANDOM	228.2 (33.10)	1.26×10^6	+1.66	+1.06	+1.36	0.254 (0.100)
2	TITANIUM 6AL-4V E.B. WELD	RANDOM	213.9 (31.02)	1.26×10^6	+1.84	+1.20	+1.51	0.254 (0.100)

1 • YIELD = 120,000 PSI
  • ULTIMATE = 130,000 PSI
  • FATIGUE @ 1.26 X 10⁶ CYCLES = 78,000 PSI
    UNNOTCHED (K_T=1.5 IS INCLUDED IN PREDICTED STRESS LEVEL)

2 @ 2.2 , 1-1/2% DAMPING, K_T = 1.5

3 PER 400 (4 LINES) MISSIONS

4 3.0 USED FOR LIMIT STRESS

Table 4. Fracture Mechanics Analyses Results

Case Number	Material	No. of Missions	Flaw cm.(Inches)		K_MAX MPA √cm̄ (KSI √in̄)	
			Depth -A	Length-C	Depth-A	Length-C
1	Titanium	Initial	0.177800 (0.070000)	0.190500 (0.0750000)	-	-
			-	-	-	-
		17	0.254* (0.100000)	0.39910 (0.157123)	169.481 (15.4214)	141.568 (12.8815)
2	Titanium	Initial	0.177800 (0.070000)	0.190500 (0.0750000)	-	-
					-	-
		400	0.177800 (0.070000)	0.190500 (0.0750000)	82.294 (7.4881)	74.951 (6.8199)

* TRANSITION TO T-C, INSTABILITY - FAILURE

It was the FLAGRO analysis which alerted Marquardt to the inadequacy of the standoff design. The results for the original design and the revised, final design are presented in Table 4. As shown, failure was predicted for Case 1, while Case 2 survives the entire 4 lives. The redesign case, Case 2, involved the following changes:

> A redundant load path was placed between the injector and the valve mounting plate in the area of the most highly stressed region of the standoff and

> All ridges, "weld suck backs" were eliminated by a cosmetic weld pass and/or mechanical grinding of the weld joint.

The standoff weld joint has not failed nor cracked in further testing.

VIII. CONCLUSIONS

The Fracture Control Plan, that was presented for the Space Shuttle Reaction Control Thrusters, proved successful by virtue of successful qualification testing. As illustrated, the Fracture Control Plan provided some of the most re- strictive criteria to which thrusters have been designed and developed. However, as restrictive as fracture mechanics applications appeared, it remained as the only analytical

tool that predicted the few repetitive structural failures
experienced in the Reaction Control Thruster development
program.

Minimizing time and cost and adhering to schedule without sacrificing structural integrity are considerations that
must be blended into a Fracture Control Plan. However, a
well conceived and implemented Fracture Control Plan, which
is created early in the development of hardware, can provide
a valuable tool to assure structural integrity.

REFERENCES

1. Materials Properties Manual, Publication No. 2543-W
   Space Division, Rockwell International, Prepared by
   Materials and Processes Group, Shuttle Engineering
   Volume 1. Effectivity June 1975 through June 1977.

2. Damage Tolerant Design Handbook, A Compilation of
   Fracture and Crack-Growth Data for High Strength
   Alloys, MC1C-MB-01, Part 2, January 1975,
   Metals and Ceramics Information Center, Battelle
   Columbus Laboratories

3. Ehret, R.M., Fracture Control Methods for Space
   Vehicles Volume II, Assessment of Fracture Mechanics
   Technology for Space Shuttle Applications,
   SD-73-SH-0171-2, January 1974, Space Division,
   Rockwell International.

A REVIEW AND ASSESSMENT OF FATIGUE CRACK GROWTH
RATE RELATIONSHIPS FOR METALLIC AIRFRAME MATERIALS

By

J. B. Chang, M. Szamossi and E. Klein
Rockwell International, North American Aircraft Division
Los Angeles, California

INTRODUCTION

The current issued aircraft structural integrity program
(ASIP) requirements levied on weapon systems that are presently in operation or under development have necessitated the
advancement of analytical methods to predict growth behaviors
of cracks or crack-like flaws contained in metallic airframe
structures under flight spectrum loadings (1). To perform
fatigue crack growth analyses, the common practice is to use
a damage accumulation package which interrelates the following elements:

1. A fatigue crack growth rate relationship and the
    corresponding fracture properties

2. Initial crack types, sizes, and geometries of the
    cracked body

3. Crack-tip stress intensity factor solutions

4. Fatigue spectrum loading descriptions

Recently, a research and development program has been
undertaken by Rockwell for the U.S. Air Force. The program
is aimed at upgrading the fatigue crack growth prediction
technology required for implementation of the damage toler-
ance control procedures throughout the life cycle of any
weapon system. To accomplish this objective, review and

evaluation of the state-of-the-art fatigue crack growth rate
relationships was deemed necessary. A specific task conducted in phase I of this program was to perform such a
review and evaluation (2). This paper summarizes the result
of this task.

STATE-OF-THE-ART

Historically, fatigue crack growth data generated from
various test programs were often recorded in the form of
crack grwoth measurements (Δa) and the corresponding cycle
counts (ΔN). The relationship between the crack size, a, and
the number of applied cycles, N, can then be represented as a
crack growth chart, as shown in Fig. 1. However, this type
of data only represents the growth behavior of a specific
crack configuration under a specific loading condition.
Therefore, it can not be directly used for performing crack
growth behavior prediction for other crack configurations and
loading conditions. To make use of such test data, it is
necessary to convert the discrete test data into a general
relationship by choosing the appropriate parameters.

The common practice of the aircraft industry in predicting the growth behavior of cracks under flight spectrum loading is to employ a crack growth analysis computer program such
as EFFGRO, developed by Rockwell, and CRACKS, developed by the
Air Force (3, 4). Fatigue crack growth methodologies implemented in many of such computer programs are based on the
linear elastic fracture mechanics (LEFM) concept. LEFM
assumes that the entire stress field at the crack tip can be
sufficiently characterized by a parameter identified as the
stress intensity factor (K). For cyclic loading conditions,
it is the range of the stress intensity factor which charac-
terizes the fatigue crack growth behavior. Customarily, the
crack growth rate per cycle (da/dN) is chosen as the dependent variable of a fatigue crack growth rate relationship
which is commonly called a growth rate equation. In the
functional form, it can be expressed as

$$da/dN = f(\Delta K)$$

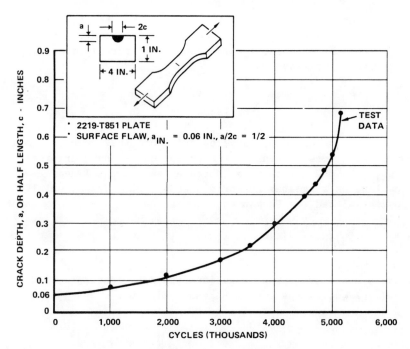

Fig. 1. Crack-Growth Curve, 2219-T851 Aluminum Plate
Containing Surface Crack Subjected to Spectrum Loading.

Paris' Equation

Many such fatigue crack growth rate equations have been
formulated by various investigators since Paris proposed the
so-called Paris' equation in the late 1950's (5). Paris'
equation is in the following simple form:

$$da/dN = C \ (\Delta K)^n$$

where C and n are the "growth rate constants" which are determined from constant-amplitude tests.

Paris' equation resulted in a straight-line presentation
on a double logarithmic scale, with ℓn (da/dN) representing
the vertical axis, and ℓn (ΔK) representing the horizontal
axis; i.e.,

$$\ell n \ (da/dN) = C + n \ell n(\Delta K)$$

In the preceding straight-line equation, the coefficient C is the growth rate intercept corresponding to a unit value of ΔK, and the exponent n corresponds to the reciprocal slope of the straight line.

Forman Equation

It was observed by many investigators that when the maximum cyclic stress intensity factor approaches some critical value, K_{cr}, the growth rate increases beyond the linear behavior, as suggested by Paris's equation. Forman, et al, thus formulated the Forman equation as

$$da/dN = C[\Delta K]^n/[(1-R)K_{cr}-\Delta K]$$

where C and n are Paris' equation-type rate constants, and $R = \sigma_{min}/\sigma_{max}$ is the cyclic stress ratio (6).

Walker Equation

As more and more test data generated from constant-amplitude loadings at different stress ratios become available, fatigue crack growth rates are obviously dependent on the stress ratio. A wide-range fatigue crack growth rate data of 2219-T851 aluminum alloy at three stress ratios is shown in Fig. 2. The stress ratio layering on crack growth data is clearly shown. To account for the stress ratio effect, Walker introduced the idea of the effective stress $\overline{\sigma}$, defined as

$$\overline{\sigma} = (1-R)^m \sigma_{max}$$

where m is an empirical constant that depends upon the material, and σ_{max} is the maximum cyclic stress (7).

Incorporating the effective stress term into Paris' equation resulted in an equation identified as the Walker equation in the open literature:

$$da/dN = C[(1-R)^m K_{max}]^n$$

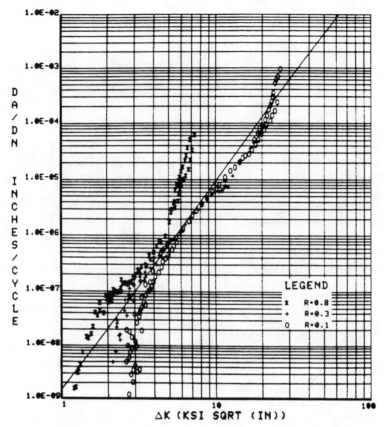

Fig. 2. Wide-Range Fatigue Crack-Growth-Rate Data of 2219-
T851 Aluminum Alloy at Various Stress Ratios (Ref. 12).

In terms of the stress intensity factor range, ΔK, the
Walker equation can be expressed as

$$da/dN = C[(1-R)^{m-1}\Delta K]^n$$

Collipriest (Sigmoidal) Equation

Crack growth data of many materials showed the characteristics of the sigmoidal (S shape) curve when plotting da/dN
versus ΔK on the double logarithmic scale. Collipriest proposed a rate equation as

$$da/dN = C(K_c \Delta K_{th})^{n/2} \times$$

$$\exp\left[\ln(K_c/\Delta K_{th})^{n/2} \tan h^{-1}\left(\frac{\ln[\Delta K^2/(1-R)K_c \Delta K_{th}]}{\ln[(1-R)K_c/\Delta K_{th}]}\right)\right]$$

where K_c is the critical value of the stress intensity factor under cyclic loading, and ΔK is the threshold stress intensity factor range (8).

Grumman (Modified Closure) Equation. Bell, et al, of Grumman Aerospace Company, proposed a crack growth rate equation which is a modified version of Elber's closure model formulated by Elber to account for the closure force effect to the crack growth (9, 10). The Grumman equation is expressed as

$$da/dN = C[(1+q\bar{R})\Delta K]^n , \qquad \begin{array}{l} R \le R_{cut} , \quad \bar{R} = R \\ \\ R > R_{cut} , \quad \bar{R} = R_{cut} \end{array}$$

where q is an empirical constant.

Boeing Equation. Hall, et al, of the Boeing Aerospace Company, have developed a crack growth rate equation in the form

$$da/dN = C(K_{max} - K_{th})^\alpha (\Delta K)^n$$

where K_{max} is the maximum cyclic stress intensity factor, K_{th} is the maximum cyclic threshold stress intensity factor, and α is a curve-fit constant (11).

Three-Component Equation. Hudak, et al, proposed a three-component equation recently to characterize three regions of crack growth (12). Region I is the low-growth region, region II is the intermediate growth region, and region III is the fast-growth region. The characteristic equation describing the crack growth rate in these three regions is given by:

$$da/dN = \left\{ \frac{A_1(R)}{(\Delta K)^{n1}} + \frac{A_2(R)}{(\Delta K)^{n_2}} - \frac{A_2(R)}{[(1-R)K_{cr}]^{n_2}} \right\}^{-1}$$

where n_1 and n_2 are constants determined from the test data, the functions $A_1(R)$ and $A_2(R)$ directly control the stress ratio dependencies in regions I and II, respectively, and the onset of instability in region III is described by $(1-R)K_{cr}$.

Rockwell (Modified Walker) Equation. Chang and his coworkers at Rockwell modified the Walker equation to account for the variable-threshold stress intensity factor range, as shown in Fig. 2 (13). The proposed equation also adopts the concept that the stress ratio effect to the crack growth has its cutoff values. Beyond this value (R_{cut}), no further stress-ratio layering will be shown. The Rockwell equation can be expressed as:

• For $\Delta K > (1-R)\Delta K_{th_o}$,

$$da/dN = C[(1-\overline{R})^{m-1}\Delta K]^n$$

$$R \leq R_{cut} \ , \quad \overline{R} = R$$

$$R > R_{cut} \ , \quad \overline{R} = R_{cut}$$

• For $\Delta K \lessgtr (1-R)\Delta K_{th_o}$

$$da/dN = 0$$

where ΔK_{th_o} is the value of the threshold stress intensity factor at $R = 0$.

FATIGUE CRACK GROWTH RATE EQUATIONS ASSESSMENTS

A number of fatigue crack growth rate equations were chosen in the predictive accuracy assessment task in order to ultimately select a single rate equation which can be implemented into the improved fatigue crack growth prediction methodology. The criterion for choosing such a candidate is that it must be easily used for hand-calculations if the analyst so desires, or if the working environment exclude the possibility of using a computer program. Three rate equations were chosen in the evaluation: the Boeing, Grumman, and Rockwell equations. The evaluation was made by performing the correlation and the cross correlation of the baseline growth rate data.

CRACK GROWTH DATA CORRELATION

In order to maintain a one-to-one comparison in the evaluation, the Rockwell in-house-developed fatigue crack growth analysis computer program, EFFGRO, was modified to provide options for selecting any of these three rate equations in the analysis. 2219-T851 aluminum alloy baseline fatigue crack growth data generated by Boeing and Grumman (documented in References 11 and 9) were selected as the primary data base. In addition, baseline crack growth data of 6Aℓ-4V titanium alloy and 9Ni-4Co-0.2C steel alloy were also used in the evaluation such that the result of the evaluation can represent most of the commonly used airframe materials. The crack specimens tested were compact-type (CT), Center-Crack-Tension (CCT), and part-through crack (PTC) specimens.

Crack growth rate constants of different materials corresponding to the three rate equations used in the correlation were those documented in the referenced reports. Table 1 summarizes these three growth rate equations and the corresponding rate constants for all materials correlated. The static and fracture properties of these materials were also summarized and are presented in Table 2.

Table 1. Summary of Crack-Growth-Rate Equations and Corresponding Growth-Rate Constants Used In Baseline Crack-Growth Data Correlations and Cross-Correlations.

Rate Equation \ Material	2219-T851 Aluminum	Ti-6A1-4V Titanium	9Ni-4Co-0.2c Steel
Boeing Equation $da/dN = C(K_{max} - K_{th})^{\alpha} (\Delta K)^{n}$	$C = 0.34 \times 10^{-8}$ $\alpha = 0.84$ $n = 2.4$ $K_{th} = 1.5$ ksi $\sqrt{in.}$	$C = 0.33 \times 10^{-10}$[b] $\alpha = 1.02$ $n = 3.0$ $K_{th} = 5$ ksi $\sqrt{in.}$	$C = 0.4 \times 10^{-8}$ $\alpha = 0.57$ $n = 1.76$ $K_{th} = 10$ ksi $\sqrt{in.}$
Grumman Equation $da/dN = C[(1 + q\overline{R})\Delta K]^{n}$ $R \leq R_{co}, \overline{R} = R$ $R > R_{co}, \overline{R} = R_{co}$	$C = 1.96 \times 10^{-9}$ $n = 3.34$ $q = 0.6$ $R_{co} = 0.5$	$C = 5.9 \times 10^{-10}$[c] $n = 3.08$ $q = 0.7$ $R_{co} = 0.7$	--
Rockwell Equation[a] $da/dN = C\left[\dfrac{\Delta K}{(1-\overline{R})^{1-m}}\right]$ $R \leq R_{co}, \overline{R} = R$ $R > R_{co}, \overline{R} = R_{co}$ $da/dN = 0, \Delta K \leq \Delta K_{th}$	$C = 1.72 \times 10^{-9}$ $n = 3.415$ $m = 0.65$ $R_{co} = 0.6$ $\Delta K_{th} = 1.5$ ksi $\sqrt{in.}$	--	--

[a] Used for cross-correlation only

[b] Beta annealed

[c] Mill annealed

Table 2. Summary of Static and Fracture Properties Used in
Baseline Crack-Growth Data Correlations and
Cross-Correlations.

Static Properties Materials		TYS (ksi)	TUS (ksi)	Elong (%)	RA (%)	E (ksi)	K_{Ic} or K_c (ksi $\sqrt{in.}$)
2219-T851 Alum	Boeing Data	52.6 (L) 51.3 (T)	66.1 (L) 66.3 (T)	16 (L) 15 (T)	28 (L) 25 (T)	10×10^3	45 (K_{Ic}) 76 (K_c)
	Grumman Data	54.7	66.9	10.3			30 (K_{Ic}) 57.5 (K_c)
	Rockwell Data[a]	48	62	8		10.5×10^3	45 (K_{Ic}) 76 (K_c)
Ti-6Al-4V	Boeing Data[b]	125.3 (L) 128 (T)	138.4 (L) 138.6 (T)	16 (L) 16 (T)	26 (L) 25 (T)		80 (K_{Ic}) 160 (K_c)
	Grumman Data[c]	130.0 (1/4 in.) 135.3 (3/4 in.)	132.6 (1/4 in.) 137.6 (3/4 in.)	17.8 (1/4 in.) 12.6 (3/4 in.)			72 (K_{Ic})
9Ni-4Co-0.2C steel	Boeing Data	185.3 (L) 186.6 (T)	203.2 (L) 203.5 (T)	23 (L) 23 (T)	56 (L) 55 (T)		140 (K_{Ic}) 180 (K_c)

[a]Used for cross-correlation only
[b]Beta annealed
[c]Mill annealed

Analytical predictions obtained from the EFFGRO program
were plotted against the experimental data in a "crack size"
versus "numbers of cycles" format for each of the correlated
cases. Typical examples of such plots are shown in Figs. 3
through 6. For the purpose of evaluation, a predictability
index (R), which is defined as the ratio of the predicted life
(N_{pred}) to the tested life (N_{test}) for each of the correlated
cases, has been calculated. Table 3 shows a typical summary
of the R values for the Grumman 2219-T851 aluminum baseline
crack growth rate data correlated.

The results of the correlations indicate that each of the
three growth rate equations and the corresponding rate constants
developed from the referenced test programs can be used to
characterize the crack growth behavior under constant-amplitude
loadings for the specific batch of materials tested. They also
demonstrate that the stress intensity factor solutions and the
numerical integration scheme employed in EFFGRO are reliable,
since the original determination of the rate constants to the
Boeing and Grumman equations was not done by EFFGRO.

45

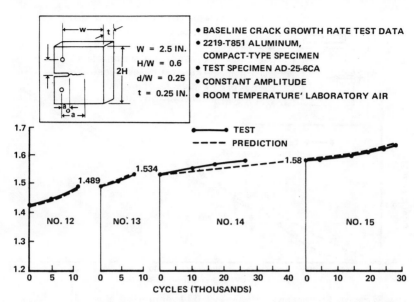

Fig. 3. Grumman 2219-T851 Aluminum Baseline Crack-Growth-
Rate Test Data Correlation, Specimen AD-25-6CA.

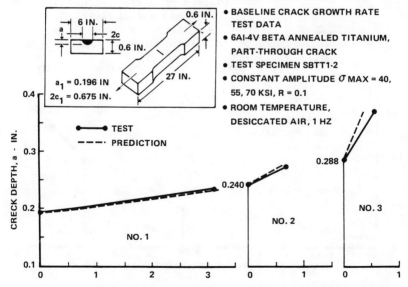

Fig. 4. Boeing Ti-6Al-4V -Annealed Baseline Crack-Growth-
Rate Data Correlation, Specimen SBTT1-2.

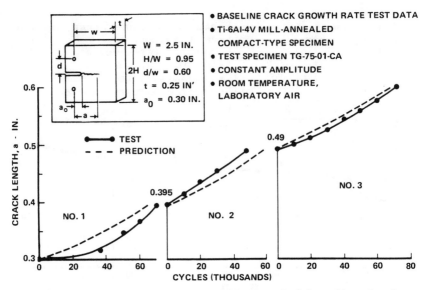

Fig. 5. Grumman Ti-6Al-4V Mill-Annealed Baseline Crack-Growth-Rate Test Data Correlation, Specimen TG-75-01.

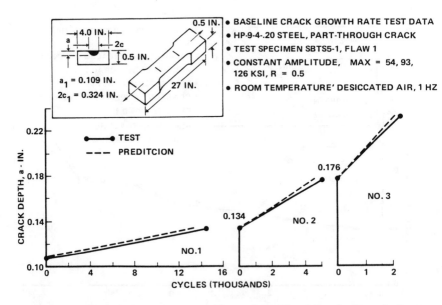

Fig. 6. Boeing HP-9-4-0.20 Steel Baseline Crack-Growth-Rate Data Correlation, Specimen SBTS5-1, Flaw 1.

Table 3. Summary, Correlation of Grumman 2219-T851 Aluminum Baseline Crack-Growth-Rate Data.

Test specimen No.	P(kips)	R	N_{Test}(cyc)	N_{Pred}(cyc)	$R = \dfrac{N_{Pred}}{N_{Test}}$	Remarks
AG-25-01-CTB 1	0.950	0.7	489,000	570,000	1.16	Grumman's
2	0.950	0.5	5,000	7,750	1.55	CT specimen
3	0.950	0.3	8,300	8,800	1.06	
4	0.500	0.1	30,450	13,250	0.43	
AG-25-02A-CTB 1	0.500	-1.0	264,160	327,000	1.24	
AG-25-20-CTB 1	0.700	-1.0	65,120	78,400	1.20	
AG-25-21-CTB 1	0.500	-1.0	286,820	250,600	0.87	
AG-25-27-CTB 1	0.420	0.05	677,400	522,000	0.77	
AG-25-29-CTB 1	0.998	0.7	195,000	122,000	0.63	
2	0.998	0	19,300	17,300	0.90	
AG-25-30-CTB 1	0.951	0.7	424,100	341,000	0.80	
2	0.951	0.5	51,900	43,000	0.83	
3	0.951	0.3	7,600	7,720	1.01	
4	0.951	0.1	2,550	1,830	0.78	
5	0.500	0.1	139,050	6,300	0.04	
6	0.500	-0.1	1,046	1,090	1.04	
AG-50-01-CTB 1	1.400	0.05	90,020	106,600	1.18	
AD-25-06-CTA 1	0.880	0.7	325,880	417,000	1.28	ASTM
2	0.880	0.5	47,607	41,100	0.86	CT specimen
3	0.710	0.3	15,210	23,800	1.56	
4	0.710	0.05	6,724	8,000	1.19	
5	0.580	0.7	131,960	215,500	1.63	
6	0.580	0.5	70,100	34,700	0.50	
7	0.490	0.3	12,275	16,800	1.38	
8	0.490	0.05	7,310	7,550	1.03	
9	0.400	0.5	36,980	61,000	1.65	
10	0.400	0.05	15,450	9,200	0.60	
11	0.330	0.3	20,540	35,230	1.71	
12	0.330	0.05	11,355	11,800	1.04	
13	0.280	-1.0	8,109	6,300	0.78	
14	0.280	0.5	26,890	38,650	1.44	
15	0.200	0.05	27,820	27,150	0.97	
AD-25-08-CTA 1	1.657	0.7	46,072	89,500	1.94	ASTM
2	1.321	0.3	2,251	1,850	0.82	CT specimen
3	1.321	0.05	892	970	1.09	
4	1.055	0.7	25,238	38,400	1.52	
5	1.055	0.5	4,006	4,300	1.07	
6	0.859	0.3	3,650	2,990	0.82	
7	0.859	0.05	1,246	1,140	0.91	
8	0.671	0.5	6,163	6,550	1.06	
9	0.671	0.05	1,145	1,010	0.88	
10	0.535	0.3	3,562	3,380	0.95	

CRACK GROWTH DATA CROSS-CORRELATIONS

Baseline fatigue crack growth data of 2219-T851 aluminum alloy generated by Boeing and Grumman were cross-correlated using the three rate equations. The objective of the cross-correlation is to assess the predictive accuracies when different fatigue crack growth rate equations and the corresponding growth rate constants were employed in the analytical predictions for one batch of material. Again, EFFGRO was used in the performance of analytical predictions. These rate equations and the corresponding growth rate constants used in the cross-correlations are shown in Table 1. The corresponding static and fracture properties are listed in Table 2.

Figs. 7 and 8 show typical results of the cross-correlations on Boeing 2219-T851 aluminum alloy baseline crack growth data. The crack growth behaviors predicted by using different rate equations were plotted against the test data. Since there is essentially no difference between the results predicted by the Rockwell and Grumman equations, only the results predicted by using the Boeing and Rockwell equations are presented. Statistics on the accuracy of the life predictions using three different fatigue crack growth rate equations and their corresponding crack growth rate constants are obtained and are presented in Table 4.

As can be seen from the table, all statistical data show that the fatigue life predictions obtained by using the Rockwell equation and growth constants are practically no different when they are compared to those obtained by using the Grumman equation and constants. There are only slight differences when they are compared to those obtained by using the Boeing equation and constants. For further illustration, histograms of the number of correlations against the ratio of the predicted life to the test life are plotted in Figure 9.

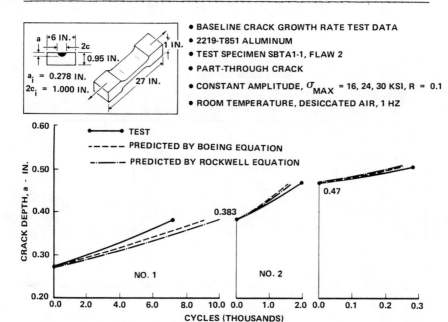

Fig. 7. Boeing 2219-T851 Aluminum Baseline Crack-Growth-Rate Data Cross-Correlation, Specimen SBTA1-1, Flaw 2.

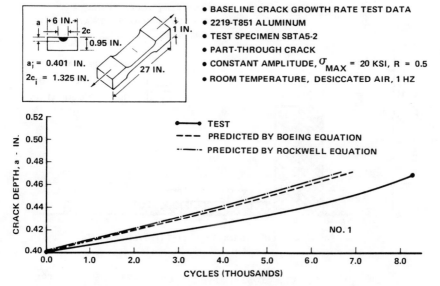

Fig. 8. Boeing 2219-T851 Aluminum Baseline Crack-Growth-Rate Data Cross-Correlation, Specimen SBTA5-2.

Table 4. Crack-Growth Cross-Correlation of Boeing 2219-
T851 Aluminum Baseline Data.

Range of R		Grumman Equation	Boeing Equation	Rockwell Equation
From	To			
0.70	1.30	68%	68%	68%
0.85	1.15	44%	36%	48%
0.70	1.00	64%	60%	56%
0.85	1.00	40%	52%	36%
Mean		1.05	1.14	1.05
Standard Deviation		0.48	0.55	0.47

$$R = \frac{N_{Pred}}{N_{Test}}$$

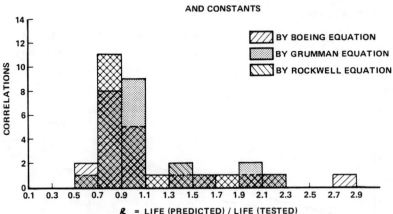

• BOEING BASELINE CRACK GROWTH RATE DATA
• 2219-T851 ALUMINUM
• CONSTANT - AMPLITUDE LOADING
• PREDICTED BY EFFGRO USING RATE EQUATION
  AND CONSTANTS

Fig. 9. Histogram, Cross-Correlation on Boeing 2219-T851
Aluminum Baseline Crack-Growth-Rate Data.

Cross-correlations also have been conducted on the Grumman 2219-T851 aluminum alloy baseline crack growth data. The same statistics on the predictive accuracy using the Boeing, Rockwell, and Grumman equations and the corresponding growth rate constants as done previously on the Boeing baseline data are presented in Table 5. Again, it can be seen that there are essentially no differences between the results predicted by the Grumman and Rockwell equations. Using the Grumman equation and the corresponding rate constants fitted by Grumman to predict back Grumman crack growth data, 76 percent of the predictions are accurate within ±30 percent. Judging by the fact that Rockwell rate constants were developed from Rockwell's fatigue crack growth data generation program, which was originally aimed in support of the application of fracture mechanics design requirements to the B-1 strategic bomber, the accuracy of the prediction is considered to be very good. Similar comments can be applied to the predicted results by using the Boeing equation and the rate constants derived by Boeing. Fig. 11 shows the accuracy of fatigue crack growth prediction with the three different rate equations.

Table 5. Crack-Growth Cross-Correlation of Grumman 2219-T851 Aluminum Baseline Data.

Range of R		Grumman Equation	Boeing Equation	Rockwell Equation
From	To			
0.70	1.30	76%	68%	73%
0.85	1.15	43%	39%	43%
0.70	1.00	40%	41%	41%
0.85	1.00	24%	22%	20%
Mean		0.99	0.84	0.98
Standard Deviation		0.30	0.36	0.31

$$R = \frac{N_{Pred}}{N_{Test}}$$

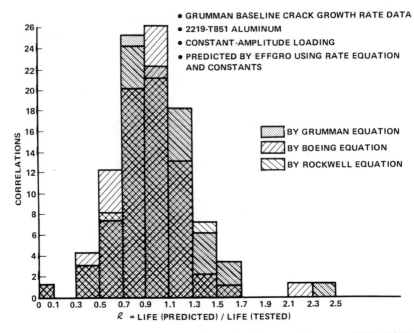

Fig. 10. Histogram, Cross-Correlation on Grumman 2219-T851 Aluminum Baseline Crack-Growth-Rate Data.

CONCLUDING REMARKS

The state-of-the-art fatigue crack growth rate equations commonly used for performing damage-tolerance analysis on airframe structures were reviewed. Three such rate equations were assessed using the baseline crack growth test data. They are the Boeing, Grumman, and Rockwell equations. Results of the assessment indicated that by properly choosing the rate constants all three equations can be used to characterize the fatigue crack growth rate relationships for airframe materials.

ACKNOWLEDGEMENTS

This report is based in part on the result of a study performed under Contract F33615-77-C-3121, sponsored by the Wright-Aeronautical Laboratories, Flight Dynamics Laboratory, Wright-Patterson Air Force Base, Ohio.

REFERENCES

(1) Anon, "Military Standard, Aircraft Structural Integrity
     Program, Airplane Requirements," MIL-STD-1530A, 1975

(2) J.B. Chang, J.H. Stolpestad, M. Shinozuka, and R. Vaicaitis,
     "Improved Methods for Predicting Spectrum Loading Effects -
     Phase I Report, Volume I - Results and Discussion,"
     AFFDL-TR-79-3036, Vol 1, Air Force Flight Dynamics
     Laboratory, Wright-Patterson AFB, Ohio, 1979

(3) M. Szamossi, "Crack Propagation Analysis by Vroman's
     Model, Program EFFGRO, "NA-72-94, Rockwell International,
     Los Angeles, 1972

(4) R.M. Engle, "CRACKS, A Fortran IV Digital Computer Program
     for Crack Propagation Analysis," AFFDL-TR-70-107, Air
     Force Flight Dynamics Laboratory, Wright-Patterson AFB,
     Ohio, 1970

(5) P.C. Paris, M.P. Gomez, and W.E. Anderson, "A Rational
     Analytic Theory of Fatigue," The Trend in Engineering,
     Vol 13, No. 1, 1961

(6) R.G. Forman, V.E. Kearney, and R.M. Engle, "Numerical
     Analysis of Crack Propagation in Cyclic-Loaded Structures,"
     J. of Basic Engineering Trans. of ASME, Vol 89, 1967

(7) K. Walker, "The Effect of Stress Ratio During Crack Propa-
     gation and Fatigue for 2024-T3 and 7075-T6 Aluminum,"
     ASTM STP462, American Society for Testing and Materials,
     1970

(8) J.E. Collipriest, and R.M. Ehret, "Computer MOdeling of
     Part-Through-Crack Growth," SD-72-CE-15, Rockwell
     International, Space Division, Downey, 1972

(9) P.D. Bell, and M. Creager, "Crack Growth Analyses for
     Arbitrary Spectrum Loading," AFFDL-TR-74-129, Air Force
     Flight Dynamics Laboratory, Wright-Patterson AFB, Ohio,
     1974

(10) W. Elber, "The Significance of Fatigue Crack Closure,"
     ASTM STP486, American Society for Testing and Materials,
     1971

(11) L.R. Hall, R.C. Shah, and W.L. Engstrom, "Fracture and
      Fatigue Crack Growth Behavior of Surface Flaws and Flaws
      Originating at Fastener Holes," AFFDL-TR-74-47, Air Force
      Flight Dynamics Laboratory, Wright-Patterson AFB, Ohio,
      1974

(12) S.J. Hudak, A. Saxener, R.J. Bucci, and R.C. Malcom,
      "Development of Standard Methods of Testing and Analyzing
      Fatigue Crack Growth Rate Data," AFML-TR-78-40, Air Force
      Materials Laboratory, Wright-Patterson AFB, Ohio, 1978

(13) J.B. Chang, "Improved Methods for Predicting Spectrum
      Loading Effects, Fifth Quarterly Report," NA-78-491-5,
      Rockwell International, Los Angeles, 1979

REMAINING LIFE PREDICTION IN THE MICROCRACK INITIATION REGIME

O. Buck, W. L. Morris, and M. R. James
Rockwell International Science Center
Thousand Oaks, California 91360

ABSTRACT

About ninety percent of the total fatigue life of common structural
alloys, which are originally free of defects, is spent in initiation and
growth of short cracks. This paper briefly reviews our present knowledge of
crack initiation and early growth, and also reviews several advanced nondestructive techniques that are useful to monitor accumulated fatigue damage.
One of these, harmonic generation of surface acoustic waves, is discussed in
more detail. A model which relates the length and density of surface microcracks to the amplitude of the harmonic signal is described. A correlation
between experimentally measured harmonic amplitude and remaining fatigue
life is then demonstrated, which allows the mean remaining fatigue life to
be estimated. Hopefully, this research will lead to a useful "Retirement-
For-Cause" strategy.

I.   INTRODUCTION

Increasing performance demands, high costs of equipment and maintenance, and intensified liability considerations impose an ever increasing
emphasis on the use of more effective nondestructive evaluation (NDE) and
maintenance procedures. Retirement of fatigue damaged high performance
components on an individual basis, at an optimum point prior to critical
failure, is potentially a cost effective strategy. A problem arises, however, when the critical crack size is small because this places special
requirements on the reliability of nondestructive (ND) tests to detect
incipient small cracks.

Traditionally, retirement strategy has followed one of two options.
In the most favorable cases, cracks are detected long before criticality.
The progression to failure is predicted using fracture mechanics, verified
by intermediate inspection, and the component is retired before criticality
is reached. If the nondestructive inspection (NDI) resolution (or reliability) is somewhat marginal as a crack approaches criticality, current practice is to retire the component when a crack is first detected. In special
cases, it has been deemed necessary to retire entire sets of components at
an expended lifetime producing detectable cracks in only a small fraction of
the components. To ensure that one can use a particular structure safely or
at least with little risk of injury or damage, is an enormous challenge to
fatigue research. As stated by Fong recently, our objectives in fatigue
research over the next 8-12 years should be to develop "a qualitative measure of fatigue damage and an associated theory of life prediction" (1).

This is, by nature, a multidisciplinary problem. In this paper, we briefly discuss research that has been carried out over the past five years at our laboratory with the above objective in mind.

Several papers in this symposium deal with the prediction of life if a relatively large flaw is present in the structure. At the present time, the sensitivity of conventional nondestructive testing techniques (dye-penetrants, magnetic particle, ultrasonic, eddy-current, and radiographic inspection) is such that surface breaking flaws of about 1 mm in length can be detected. Assuming then that a periodic fatigue load of constant amplitude or repetitive load blocks (of varying load within each block) will be applied to the structure, fatigue crack growth equations can be used to calculate the remaining numbers of load cycles, or load blocks, until ultimate failure of the structure occurs as determined by the fracture toughness of the material. It is clear, however, that fatigue damage in the material occurs long before a relatively large surface breaking crack can be generated.

Scanning electron microscope (SEM) studies carried out at our laboratory on smooth fatigue specimens of high-strength aluminum alloys have led to a (simplified) scheme for the development of failure, which is given in Table 1. In the materials of interest, microcrack-initiation occurs mainly by fracture of brittle intermetallic particles near the surface.* The SEM enables us to follow the growth of cracks as small as 10 μm in length. For example, Fig. 1 shows a microcrack, developed at an intermetallic particle in a high-strength 2219-T851 aluminum alloy. It is typical of the largest cracks observed after 30% of the alloy's fatigue life has been expended during low cycle fatigue. The coalescence of two (or more) such microcracks commonly leads to formation of a macroscopic crack, which eventually terminates the life of the structure. Over a wide range in cyclic stress amplitudes the first (roughly) 90% of the total fatigue life of smooth-bar specimens occurs before the terminal crack is formed, after which conventional fracture mechanics can be applied.

Several techniques have been discussed recently that have proven (or may someday prove) to be sufficiently sensitive to detect the initiation of microcracks, their early growth and coalescence during fatigue loading (2). Table 2 summarizes several of these techniques, and their ability to detect microcracks and, in some cases, to detect the precursors to microcrack formation. For more details, the interested reader is referred to Ref. (2).

Table 1. Development of Microcracks in a Smooth, High-Strength Aluminum Alloy (Low Cycle Fatigue)

Expended Fatigue Life, %	Stage of Failure	Mean Crack Size
0-10	Cracking inside intermetallic particles	10-20 μm
20-50	Crack propagation out of intermetallics	20-100 μm
60-70	Crack interaction with grain boundaries	100 μm
80-90	Crack coalescence	500 μm
100	Failure	Specimen dimension

* Other types of initiation, for instance at grain boundaries, twins, persistent slip bands, etc., are also possible but will not be discussed here.

Recently, we have applied one of these techniques, acoustic harmonic generation, to monitor initiation and growth of surface cracks in the length regime of 10 to 500 μm. In the following, the technique, some experimental results, and a method for life prediction are briefly discussed. We believe, that this research is one of the first attempts to arrive at a theory of life prediction that is valid for the microcrack initiation phase. As such, it encompasses a much greater range of the total fatigue life than the present state-of-the-art life prediction which focusses on the growth regime, described by conventional fracture mechanics.

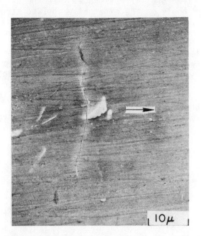

Fig. 1 Microcrack initiation in an aluminum alloy at a brittle intermetallic surface inclusion. Arrow points along the fatigue-loading axis.

Table 2. Applicability of Various NDE Techniques to Monitor Dislocation Density and Arrangement, and to Detect Microcrack Formation and Growth During Fatigue (a)

Technique	Dislocation Density/ Arrangement	Microcrack Formation/ Growth
Acoustic attenuation by dislocations	Prob. dem.	-
Acoustic transmission/reflection by interfaces	-	Dem.
Acoustic scattering	-	Prob. dem.
Acoustic harmonic generation	Dem.	Dem.
Acoustic emission	Prob. dem.	Prob. dem.
Surface topography (acoustical)	Poss.	Poss.
Surface topography (optical)	Dem.	Dem.
Photostimulated exo-electron emission	Dem.	Dem.
Positron annihilation	Dem.	-
Eddy-current techniques	Poss.	Prob. dem.
Gage concept	Poss.	Dem.

(a) Prob. dem. = probably demonstrated. Dem. = demonstrated.
    Poss. = possible.

II. MEASUREMENTS AND RESULTS

The generation of a second harmonic signal during passage of a fundamental acoustic wave along the surface of a fatigued high strength aluminum
alloy has been reported in detail (3,4). An enhanced generation of a second
harmonic with increasing fatigue was observed, and attributed to an increased anelasticity of the surface due to the development of surface microcracks. Richardson has described how such harmonics can be generated by a
simple analog of a crack, consisting of an unbonded interface between two
semi-infinite media (5). His analysis shows that the efficiency of harmonic
generation depends strongly on the externally applied stress amplitude, and
that under optimum conditions (close to zero applied stress) the second
harmonic amplitude can be as large as 17% of the fundamental.

In the experiments, a tapered flexural-fatigue specimen geometry was
employed. The tapered geometry produces a uniform surface stress, and thus
a homogeneous density of fatigue cracks over the gage section. Both specimen geometry and acoustic transducer position are illustrated in Fig. 2.
The transducers were mounted outside the gage section. To further reduce
strain at the transducer mounting locations, these parts of the specimen
were backed with 1 cm thick steel plates. The specimens (Al 7075-T6 material, given a mechanical surface polish) were fatigued in stroke control. A
strain-gaged arm in the load train was used to measure the bending moment
applied to a specimen, from which the surface stress was calculated after
calibration.

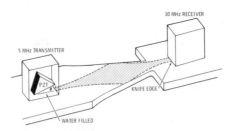

Fig. 2 Schematic illustration of the flexural fatigue
specimen showing transducer locations.

The 5 and 10 MHz PZT transducers were mounted onto fused quartz
wedges. The wedge angle, θ, in Fig. 2, measured relative to the specimen
surface, was adjusted to achieve optimum conditions for transmitting and
receiving of surface acoustic waves. Bottomless boxes containing the wedges
were attached to the specimens with an acyritate cement, and were filled
with water so that the specimen and the transducer were acoustically
coupled. A crude map of the area on the specimen from which the high-
amplitude portion of the second harmonic was received is shown in Fig. 2.

Prior to fatigue both transducers were adjusted for maximum surface-
wave signal at 10 MHz. The amplitude of the fundamental signal for an un-
fatigued specimen was found to be essentially independent of the applied
stress.

Harmonic generation measurements were made on Al 7075-T6 specimens fatigued at a maximum cyclic surface stress σ_{max} of 59, 76, and 90% of the materials yield strength, σ_{yield} (σ_{yield} = 400 MNm^{-2} for the alloy). A typical result at σ_{max} = 0.9 σ_{yield} is shown in Fig. 3. Plotted as a function of surface stress is the relative second harmonic amplitude, i.e., the ratio of the amplitude after N fatigue cycles over the amplitude before fatigue at the same surface stress. The data of Fig. 3 were obtained for a constant transmitted amplitude (i.e., for a fixed peak-to-peak driving voltage at the transmitter).

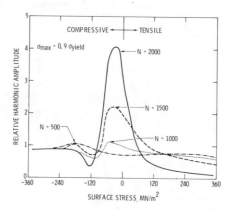

Fig. 3 Dependence of relative harmonic amplitude on surface stress and fatigue for σ_{max} = 0.9 σ_{yield}.

The central feature of the data in Fig. 3 is a second harmonic signal which increases with N at a slightly compressive stress. The same general character of the second harmonic response to the applied stress level has been found at all cyclic surface stresses used in fatiguing the specimens. A summary of these results is shown in Fig. 4, in which the peak value of

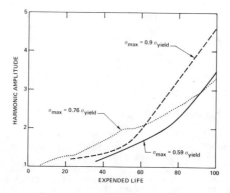

Fig. 4 Relationship between harmonic amplitude A_2 and percentage of
life expended in initiation for three values of cyclic stress.

the relative second harmonic amplitude is given as a function of the percent of expended life in the formation of the first crack of length 500 μm (see Table 1).

Richardson's analysis predicts that harmonic waves will be generated only from a small zone within a partially closed microcrack, where the fracture surfaces contact at a small normal load. Harmonic waves are generated as the crack opens and closes in the presence of an acoustic wave. Such a region of area, ΔS, is illustrated schematically in Fig. 5 (dark band); it lies inside a surface microcrack at the boundary between regions where the crack is fully opened and fully closed. Based upon compliance measurements, a semi-qualitative relationship for ΔS as a function of the crack length, 2c, has been obtained, yielding (6)

$$\Delta S \propto (2c)^2 . \tag{1}$$

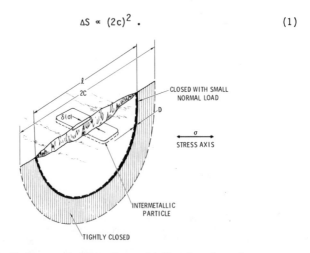

Fig. 5 Representation of a partially closed crack.

At zero external stress, the incremental harmonic signal amplitude, ΔA_{2m}, developed by a microcrack, is proportional to ΔS. Furthermore, it is proportional to A_1^n, where A_1 is the fundamental amplitude at the microcrack (3). Thus

$$\Delta A_{2m} \propto A_1^n (2c)^2 . \tag{2}$$

The exponent n lies between 2 and 5 (3).

Naturally, the location of the zone of generation is a function of the externally applied stress, σ. Its location also will vary with a quantity $\bar{\sigma}_{cc}$, known as the average crack closure stress. $\bar{\sigma}_{cc}$ is approximately equal to the tensile stress for which the zone of generation lies at the true crack front (i.e., the crack is fully open at stresses greater than $\bar{\sigma}_{cc}$). $\bar{\sigma}_{cc}$ is known to depend substantially upon the position of a surface microcrack relative to the grain boundaries (7). Consequently, the size and location of the zone of harmonic generation inside a microcrack will vary from crack to crack as well as with the externally applied stress.

We define the harmonic generation efficiency to be

$$\beta = \frac{A_{2m} + A_{2D}}{A_{2D}} \quad . \tag{3}$$

A_{2m} is the harmonic signal generated by microcracks in a surface element in the path of the surface acoustic wave and A_{2D} is the harmonic signal from other sources (8,9). The latter is given by

$$A_{2D} \propto \Delta\gamma A_1^2, \tag{4}$$

where $\Delta\gamma$ is the area of the specimen surface element contributing to harmonic generation. A_{2m} must be calculated by integration over the contributions from all microcracks in the surface element and, in the case of Al 7075-T6 is found to be, using Eq. 2,

$$A_{2m} = \xi\Delta\gamma\, A_1^n \int_0^{2c_{max}} 2c\, \Lambda(2c)\, d(2c) \quad . \tag{5}$$

$\Lambda(2c)$ is the number of cracks of length $(2c)$ per cm^2 per unit crack length, so that the quantity

$$\int_0^{2c_{max}} 2c\, \Lambda(2c)\, d(2c) = \Gamma \tag{6}$$

can be interpreted as the total crack length per cm^2, intercepted by the acoustic beam. The term ξ in Eq. (5) is a material parameter that denotes the second harmonic amplitude generated by each active element of the microcrack.

A simple analytical expression can be obtained to estimate remaining fatigue lifetime for Al 7075-T6. Pearson has suggested that the average rate of growth of surface microcracks can be approximated by

$$\frac{d(2c)}{dN} = A\Delta K, \tag{7}$$

where A is a material parameter and ΔK is the stress intensity range (10). Using the relationship $\Delta K \propto \sqrt{2c}$, integration of Eq. (7) (for an individual crack) yields

$$2c \propto N^2, \tag{8}$$

where N is the number of fatigue cycles after nucleation of the crack. Suppose that at N_F fatigue cycles the number of cracks/cm^2 and of length $2c'$ is $\Lambda_F(2c')$. At an earlier point in the lifetime, after N fatigue cycles, the length of each crack, $2c$, will simply be $2c'(N/N_F)^2$ as indicated by Eq. (8). Ignoring new cracks which develop between N and N_F cycles, the total crack length at N cycles is then given by

$$\Gamma(N) = (N/N_F)^2 \, \Gamma(N_F) \quad . \tag{9}$$

Combining Eqs. (3)-(5) and (9), the expended fatigue life is

$$\frac{N}{N_F} = \left[\frac{\beta(N)-1}{\xi \, A_1^{(n-2)} \Gamma(N_F)} \right]^{1/2} \quad . \tag{10}$$

The amplitude A_1 may be measured at the receiver, as long as the attenuation is negligible, which is approximately true for zero external stress (3).

Predictions of harmonic generation efficiency for Al 7075-T6 (Eq. (5)) have been tested, using the experimental data of Fig. 4, for a maximum cyclic stress amplitude of 90% of the yield strength, with the result shown in Fig. 6. Each datum represents a different interval during fatigue. The highest efficiency point corresponds to 2250 fatigue cycles (completion of the early growth phase). The quantity $\Gamma(N)$ has been predicted using a Monte Carlo simulation of microcrack nucleation and growth described elsewhere (7). Crack nucleation and growth parameters used in the simulation have been adjusted to obtain agreement between simulated and experimentally measured data, once the longest crack has grown to a size of about 0.5 mm. The simulation is then used to predict $\Gamma(N)$ at all other fatigue increments.

The results of Fig. 6 confirm that harmonic generation efficiency for Al 7075-T6 is essentially proportional to the total surface crack length in the inspected area. The predicted values of $\Gamma(N)$ have also been used to test Eq. (9), which relates the integrated surface crack length to the number of applied fatigue cycles. Again, the comparison is made for fully reversed fatigue loading, with a maximum cyclic stress amplitude of 90% of the yield strength. As shown in Fig. 7, Eq. (9) satisfactorily predicts the dependence of integrated crack length on fatigue for, approximately, the final 50% of the fatigue lifetime. The fact that the expression departs from expected values early in the lifetime can be attributed to the approxi-

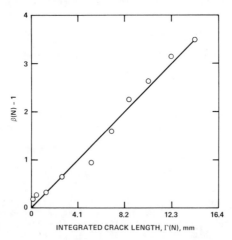

Fig. 6 Measured harmonic generation efficiency as a function of total crack length, $\Gamma(N)$.

mation that the total number of fatigue cracks on the surface is constant
throughout the specimen lifetime.

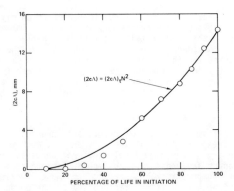

Fig. 7 Integrated crack length, $\Gamma(N)$, as a function of expended life in
initiation at $\sigma_{max} = 0.9 \, \sigma_{yield}$. Curve is the predicted $\Gamma(N)$ from
Eq. 9.

III. DISCUSSION

Equation (10) provides an estimate of the mean remaining fatigue
lifetime if N_F is taken to be the mean number of cycles to complete the
crack initiation phase. Equation (10) is used to predict the mean remaining
fatigue lifetime from β-values given in Fig. 6. A comparison of known to
predicted remaining lifetime for Al 7075-T6 is made in Fig. 8. The
agreement is satisfactory even for harmonic measurements made very early in
the fatigue lifetime.

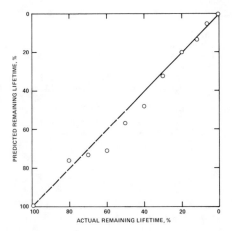

Fig. 8 Comparison of the predicted remaining fatigue life, determined from
harmonic generation data, versus the actual remaining life.

It should be added, however, that an absolute determination of remaining fatigue lifetime cannot be obtained from harmonic measurements as described here. The technique measures an integrated contribution from all the microcracks present. It is essentially insensitive to the presence or absence of an individual, extremely long microcrack which may lead to early component failure. (Very large cracks can of course be imaged with harmonics as well as at the fundamental frequency but involves different signal processing than is considered here.) On the other hand, the relationship between maximum crack length and integrated crack length can be described by a probability density function which presently is most easily found by use of a Monte Carlo simulation of crack initiation (7). Using such a probability distribution, one can then predict the probability of component failure for each additional increment in fatigue, after a harmonic measurement has been made.

Although we have achieved some progress in predicting the remaining life of components exposed to a fatigue environment, much work remains to be done. In particular, we envision developing procedures to predict the probability of component failure during subsequent fatigue loading after each inspection of this component. These predictions must involve probabilistic representations of both the fatigue failure and of the nondestructive measurement process. Having successfully completed such a prediction formalism, a next target will be the development of a multi-decision formalism by which optimal decisions concerning possible control actions could be made, based upon the past history of measurements and control actions. Such control actions may take several forms: the selection of nondestructive measurements, reassignment of duty, retirement-for-cause, or a decision that the component can be used safely as in the past.

REFERENCES

(1)   J. T. Fong, ASTM Standardization News 8, No. 2, 11 (1980).
(2)   O. Buck and G. A. Alers, in "Fatigue and Microstructure," M. Meshii, ed., American Society for Metals, 1979, p. 101.
(3)   W. L. Morris, O. Buck, and R. V. Inman, J. Appl. Phys. 50, 6737 (1979).
(4)   O. Buck, W. L. Morris, and J. M. Richardson, Appl. Phys. Letts. 33, 371 (1978).
(5)   J. M. Richardson, Int. J. Eng. Sci. 17, 83 (1979).
(6)   O. Buck, W. L. Morris and M. R. James, "Remaining Fatigue Life Prediction in the Initiation Regime Using SAW NDE," J. Nondestructive Testing (Accepted for publication).
(7)   W. L. Morris, M. R. James, and O. Buck, "Computer Simulation of Fatigue Crack Initiation," Eng. Fract. Mech. (Accepted for publication).
(8)   M. A. Breazeale and D. O. Thompson, Appl. Phys. Letts. 3, 77 (1963).
(9)   A. Hikata, B. Chick, and C. Elbaum, J. Appl. Phys. 36, 299 (1965).
(10) S. Pearson, Eng. Fract. Mech. 7, 235 (1975).

MICROSTRUCTURE AND TOUGHNESS IN
ULTRA HIGH STRENGTH STEELS

M.S. Bhat
V.F. Zackay
Department of Materials Science and Mineral Engineering
University of California, Berkeley CA 94720

ABSTRACT

The various microstructural features found in heat treated medium carbon, low and medium alloy ultra-high strength
steels are described. The fine scale details of microstructure have been identified using modern analytical tools such
as the transmission and scanning electron microscopes. These
microstructural features play a significant role in controlling the mechanical properties such as strength, toughness,
fatigue resistance, etc. In this paper, the complex role of
microstructure in the fracture of wrought ultra-high strength
steels is discussed in detail.

INTRODUCTION

The ultra high strength class of structural steels is defined as steels with yield strengths between 130-350 ksi [1].
This wide range of strengths is obtainable in a number of dis-
tinctly different types of steels as shown in Table 1. Most
of them are hardenable by heat treatment and are usually hard-
ened to the desired strength level following a fabrication
process. In this paper only two of the families listed in the
table i.e. low and medium alloy steels, are discussed. The
toughness of these steels is drastically affected by the melting [2,3] and hotworking practices [4] used before heat treatment, and also by thermomechanical processing [5,6]. However,
a discussion of the role of these techniques in controlling
toughness is beyond the scope of this paper.

The mechanical properties of interest in ultra high strength
steels are shown in Table II. These properties are a function
of the physical and chemical factors as well as microscopic
variables. Temperature, state of stress, strain rate, and en-

vironment play important roles, as do microscopic variables which are composition, crystal structure and microstructure. For a given composition, the heat treatment determines the phases present and morphologies.

Table I.   Types of Ultra High Strength Steels

A.   Medium Carbon Low Alloy Steels (e.g. 4340, 300M, HP310)

B.   Medium Alloy Steels (e.g. H11, H13)

C.   High Alloy Steels (e.g. Maraging steels, HP9-4-30)

D.   Hardenable Stainless Steels (e.g. AFC77, 17-4PH)

E.   Cold Rolled Austenitic Steels (e.g. AISI 301, AISI 201)

Table II.   Mechanical Properties of Interest
in Ultra High Strength Steels

A.   Strength (Yield and Ultimate Strength)

B.   Ductility (Reduction in Area, Elongation)

C.   Impact Toughness

D.   Fracture Toughness

E.   Stress Corrosion Cracking Resistance

F.   Fatigue Resistance

G.   Creep/Stress Rupture Strength

The elements comprising steel are of two types; alloying elements and impurities. The former are added in definite amounts for specific effects and the latter are present at levels determined by the melting practice. Alloy elements determine the type of crystal structure and microstructure obtained by heat treatment. The impurity elements usually cause a deterioration in toughness by either segregating at grain boundaries or by forming large nonmetallic inclusions [2,3,7-9].

The availability of sophisticated new instruments such
as the transmission and scanning electron microscopes
has made it possible to correlate the fine scale microstructural features with the mechanical properties. Studies at the
author's laboratory and at other laboratories have demonstrated the importance of identifying the fine details of microstructure [10-36].

In this paper an attempt has been made to review the role
of microstructure, as affected by composition and heat treatment, in controlling the fracture toughness of medium carbon,
low alloy, and medium alloy ultra-high strength steels (UHSS).

II. MICROSTRUCTURAL FEATURES IN MEDIUM C LOW
AND MEDIUM ALLOY UHSS

The microstructural features which control mechanical
properties are shown in Table III. Generally at least two or
three of these features are present.

A. Matrix Structure

Depending upon the heat treatment used, the matrix structure can consist of martensite, bainite or ferrite. Although
pearlite can also be formed by transforming the austenite at
elevated temperatures, it is generally not present in heat-
treated UHSS.

Martensite can be of two types - lath martensite and
plate [37-39]. Lath martensite is characterized by a high
dislocation density substructure, as shown in Figure 1. Plate
martensite exhibits a twinned substructure as shown in Figure
2. The composition of the steel, especially the carbon content, determines the type of martensite that is formed. In
general, plate martensite is formed in steels of high alloy
and high C content that are usually found to have low transformation temperatures. Lath martensite is generally formed
in steels which have low alloy, low carbon contents and which
have relatively high transformation temperatures. Martensite
can exist in three different states, i.e., untempered, auto-
tempered and tempered. Untempered martensite is formed in
steels which are cooled at very high rates from the austenite
field and in steels which have low transformation temperatures.
No carbides are present in the substructure of untempered
martensite. This substructure is usually very hard, in a
highly strained state, and is brittle. Auto-tempered marten-

site is found in most as-quenched steels cooled at conventional rates, e.g. oil quenching, and in steels having high transformation temperatures.

Table III. Microstructural Features in Ultra High Strength Steels	
A.	Matrix Structure (Martensite, Bainite, Ferrite)
B.	Retained Austenite
C.	Carbides
D.	Inclusions
E.	Grain Size

The auto-tempered martensite substructure will contain carbides [40,23,33]. Determining the composition of these auto-
tempered carbides is generally very difficult because the
particles are so small, but in some instances they have been
analysed. Both ε carbide and cementite have been identified
[23,27,37]. Figures 1 and 3 show examples of "wavy" and
"cross-hatched" carbides in a modified 4340 type steel. Similar carbide morphologies have been observed by Rao who identified them as ε carbide [33]. Goolsby and others have reported the precipitation of cementite in as-quenched secondary hardening steels as shown in Figure 4 [23]. Upon tempering the quenched steel different types of carbides can be
precipitated. Thus, tempered martensite, depending upon the
composition and the tempering temperature, may have ε carbide,
cementite, alloy carbides, and in some instances even intermetallic compounds precipitated in its sub-structure [41-44].
Epsilon carbides are wavy in morphology and generally precipitate on $(100)_M$ planes upon tempering at low temperatures as
shown in Figure 5 [45,46]. Elements such as Si and Al can
extend the range of temperature in which ε carbides are
stable [30,45-48]. At higher tempering temperatures cementite precipitates from the martensite matrix, usually on (110)
planes in lath martensite and (112) planes in twinned martensite [49-54]. An example of cementite precipitation in tempered martensite is shown in Figure 6.

Bainite can be of two types: upper bainite and lower
bainite [55-58]. Upper bainite consists of ferrite laths
with carbides precipitated along the lath boundaries as shown
in Figure 7. Upper bainite is formed by transformation of
the austenite in the upper bainite temperature region.

Figure 1.   Transmission electron micrograph obtained
             from as-quenched 4340+3Al steel showing
             lath martensite with high dislocation den-
             sity (A), wavy autotempered carbides (C),
             and some microtwinning (B).

Lower bainite, formed by transformation at lower temperatures,
exhibits a structure in which carbides are precipitated within ferrite laths at an angle of 55-60° to the major axis of
the lath as shown in Figure 8.

    Ferrite can be present in the microstructure of UHSS in
three different ways. It can be present as the matrix (following tempering of the martensite) when all the carbides
are precipitated and the tetragonal structure of the martensite is lost at higher tempering temperatures. It can also
be present as a soft phase in austenite at the conventional
austenitizing temperatures, due to the presence of the large
amounts of ferrite stabilizing elements such as Si, Al, Mo,
W, etc, as shown in Figure 9. Ferrite can also be formed as

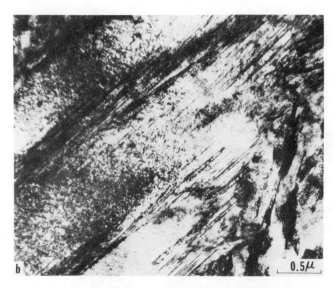

Figure 2.   Transmission electron micrograph of
martensite plates in an as-quenched
4340 steel specimen showing extensive
fine transformation twins.

the result of proeutectoid decomposition upon cooling steels
of insufficient hardenability from the austenite field as
shown in Figure 10.   In both of these latter instances the
ferrite is present as a second phase rather than as a major
matrix phase.

B.   Retained Austenite

The austenite remaining in the steel following austenitizing is called retained austenite.   The amount of retained
austenite present in the steel depends upon the composition,
the austenitization temperature and time, and the cooling
cycle used from the austenitization temperature [59-62,26-36].
The morphology of the retained austenite observed in UHSS has
been shown by transmission electron microscopy generally to
be in the form of thin films located at lath boundaries [63,
64,26-36].   This is shown in Figure 11, for quenched and
tempered steel, and in Figure 12 for slowly cooled steels.
A similar morphology has also been observed in isothermally
transformed steels [93]. Large amounts of retained austenite
may appear in the form of islands surrounded by martensite,

Figure 3. Transmission electron micrograph obtained
from as-quenched 4340+3Al steel showing
"cross-hatched" autotempered carbides.

bainite, or ferrite [65,66]. The stability of the retained
austenite determines the transformation products which may
form as a result of refrigeration, tempering or application
of stress/strain [59-63,67]. Thus, stability of the austenite can be either thermal or mechanical. Thermal stability
refers to the ability of the austenite to resist transformation
upon refrigeration or tempering, and mechanical stability
refers to its ability to resist transformation during elastic
or plastic straining. The stability of the austenite can be
influenced by three different stabilization processes. These
stabilization processes are termed (a) chemical stabilization, (b) thermal stabilization, and (c) mechanical stabilization; these terms have been defined in the literature
[67-75]. At the present time, how or why each of these

processes effects the mechanical and thermal stability of
retained austenite is not entirely clear.

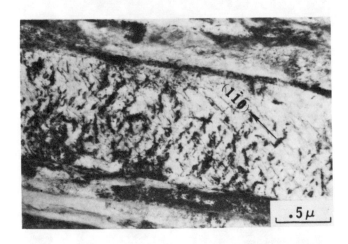

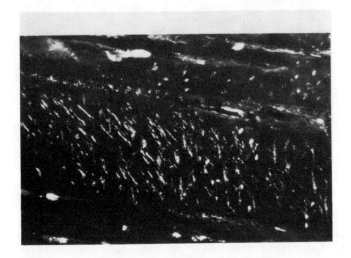

Figure 4.   Bright and dark field transmission
electron micrographs of as-quenched Fe-
0.3C-5Mo steel showing auto-tempered cementite within a martensite lath. The dark
field was obtained by using a cementite
reflection.

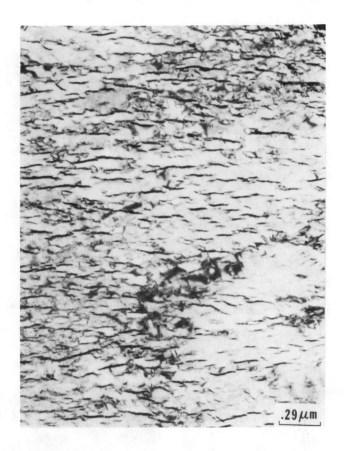

Figure 5.   Transmission electron micrograph of a
quenched and tempered experimental secondary hardening steel containing silicon
showing wavy ε carbides.

C.   Carbides

The carbides present in heat treated UHSS are of two
types: undissolved alloy carbides present in the austenite
prior to quenching, or carbides precipitated during tempering.   Generally in medium carbon low alloy steels the composition is adjusted to prevent the presence of large undissolved carbides at conventional austenitizing temperatures.
However, in some steels fine alloy carbides such as vanadium
carbide may be introduced by the addition of vanadium to
promote grain refinement.

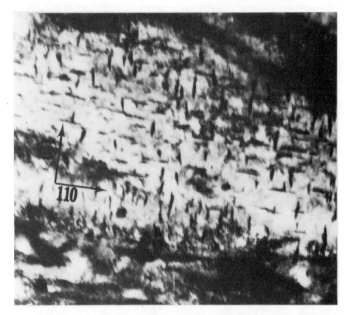

Figure 6.   Transmission electron micrograph of tempered martensite showing $(110)_M$ Widmanstatten
cementite platelets in an experimental Fe-
Cr-C steel.

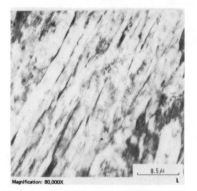 

Figure 7.   Bright and dark field electron micrographs showing upper bainite structure
in an isothermally transformed Fe-4Cr-
0.34C steel. The dark field shows re-
versal of contrast for films of carbides
at the ferrite lath boundaries.

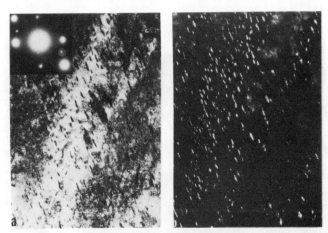

Figure 8. Bright and dark field electron micrographs
showing a lower bainite structure in an
experimental Fe-Cr-C steel. The dark
field reveals carbide precipitation 55-60°
to the lath axis.

These fine undissolved alloy carbides are not expected to
alter the mechanical properties directly; they alter mechanical properties indirectly by controlling the grain size.
Large undissolved carbides can be present following austenitization in medium alloy secondary hardening steels, and
such particles can alter mechanical properties. An example
is shown in Figures 13.

The carbides precipitated on tempering can be either
iron carbides or alloy carbides. The iron carbides usually
observed in UHSS are ε carbides (as shown in Figure 5) and
cementite Fe_3C (as shown in Figure 6). In the presence of
alloying elements a number of carbides can form depending
upon the tempering temperature and time used in the heat treatment cycle. These are $M_3C, M_7C_3, M_{23}C_6, MC, M_6C$ and M_2C, where M
refers to iron and/or other alloying elements present in the
carbide [76]. The details of their composition, crystal
structure and stability have been discussed in detail by several authors and will not be dealt with in this paper [43,76-
78].

Carbides have a different crystal structure from that of
the martensite matrix and are usually precipitated on heterogeneous sites such as grain boundaries, lath boundaries, twin
boundaries and dislocations. Iron carbides generally precipitate within the laths of martensite in certain crystallo-

graphic planes and grow in certain crystallographic directions.

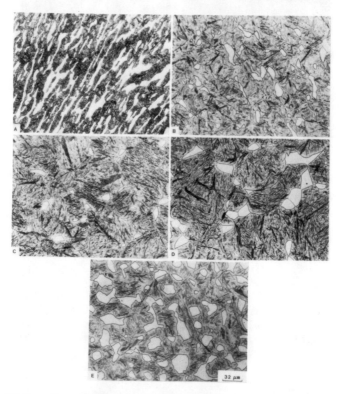

Figure 9.   Optical micrographs of a 4340+3Al steel
             austenitized at (a) 900°C, (b) 1100°C, (c)
             1150°C, (d) 1200°C, and (e) 1300°C showing
             the variation in light etching ferrite
             phase with austenitizing temperatures.

However, in twinned martensite, precipitation of cementite
can occur at the twin boundaries [54]. When the cementite
is formed as a decomposition product of austenite, it tends
to appear as continuous films at lath and grain boundaries
[10,12,19,23,31,25,79,80]. Thus, in upper bainite cementite
forms as thin continuous networks between ferrite laths as
was shown in Figure 7. In tempered martensite, tempered to
thermally decompose retained austenite, the cementite also
forms thin networks of carbide as shown in Figure 14. These
carbides are called interlath carbides; the ones which precipitate within the laths are called intralath carbides [79].
Alloy carbides can precipitate both as intralath and interlath carbides as shown in Figure 15.

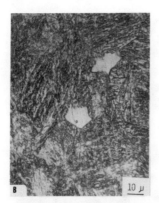

Figure 10. Optical micrograph of a low alloy steel showing the presence of light etching ferrite grains following a slow cooling treatment.

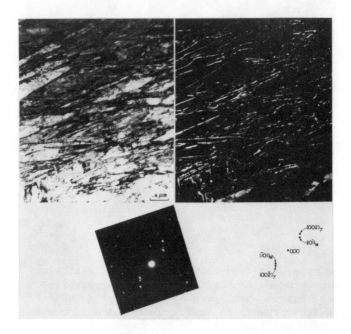

Figure 11. Transmission electron micrographs obtained from 4340+1.5Al+1.5Si steel in the as-quenched condition. The dark field picture was taken with an austenite reflection.

Figure 12. Transmission electron micrographs revealing the presence of interlath
retained austenite films in an air
cooled 2.5cm thick air cooled 300 M
steel.

D. Inclusions

The type, size and volume fraction of inclusions present
in steel depend on composition and melting practice. Modern
melting techniques have reduced the size and volume fraction
of inclusions present in UHSS. Some of the common inclusions
observed are sulfides and oxides. An example of a sulfide
inclusion is shown in Figure 16. In vacuum melted steels
the inclusion levels are kept low and the inclusions normally are small and rounded [2,12]. When elements such as Al
and Si are added to the steel, oxides of different shapes
and sizes can form [30]. An example of an aluminum oxide
inclusion is shown in Figure 17.

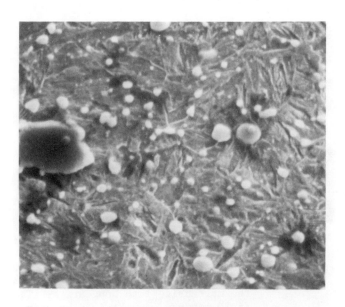

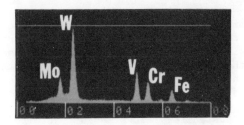

Figure 13. Scanning electron micrograph of a commercial medium alloy steel (Vasco Matrix
MA) showing the presence of large undissolved carbides. The energy dispersive
x-ray analysis peaks reveal that the carbides are rich in W, Mo, V and Cr.

E. Grain Size

In UHSS, grain size commonly refers to the prior austenite grain size which can be revealed by appropriate etching
techniques. Although the observed grain boundaries in the
final heat treated conditions are not "real", they have a
strong effect on mechanical properties.

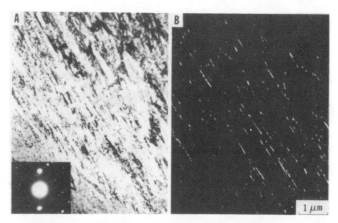

Figure 14.   Transmission electron micrographs of an
             experimental quenched and tempered second-
             ary hardening steel (tempered at 300 °C)
             showing the presence of carbide films at
             the martensite lath boundaries. The dark
             field picture was obtained by using a car-
             bide reflection.

The reasons for this are: (a) that segregation of impurity
elements can occur at the prior austenite boundaries [8,9,81],
(b) that undesirable austenite transformation products can
be formed at the boundaries [10,17,80], and (c) that the prior
austenite grain size controls the size of the transformation
products formed upon cooling [34].

     The prior austenite grain size is controlled by compo-
sition and by adjusting austenitization temperature and time
(higher temperatures and longer times lead to larger grain
sizes). By having appropriate alloy carbide formers such as
V or Nb, which are stable to high temperatures, grain growth
can be reduced [1]. In addition, the presence of inclusions
such as AlN and Al_2O_3 restricts grain growth [82,83]. The
range of prior austenite grain size normally obtained in UHSS
is from ASTM 8-5.

                III.   CORRELATION OF MICROSTRUCTURE
                    WITH TOUGHNESS IN UHSS

     Effective correlation of microstructure with mechanical
properties has been the subject of many investigations and

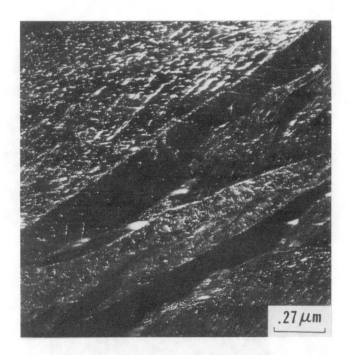

Figure 15. Dark field transmission electron micro-
            graph of an experimental quenched and
            tempered secondary hardening steel (temper-
            ed at 550 °C) showing the presence of both
            interlath and intralath molybdenum carbides.

numerous papers available in the literature have sought to
identify different microstructural features that control
toughness [10-36,79,80]. Attempts have been made to classify
these microstructural features as being either beneficial or
detrimental to strength and toughness [84-87]. Impressive
advances have been made through the increased use of research
techniques such as transmission and scanning electron microscopy in interrelating microstructure, strength, fracture
toughness and the micro-mechanisms of fracture.

A. Role of Matrix Structure

     The matrix structure that gives the best combination of
strength and toughness at carbon levels of $\leq$ 0.4 wt pct is
tempered martensite.

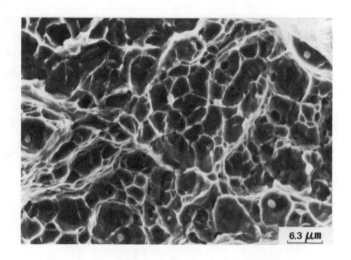

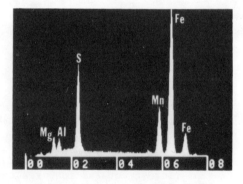

Figure 16.   Scanning electron fractograph showing
small rounded sulphide inclusions
in a 4340+3Al quenched and tempered
steel.

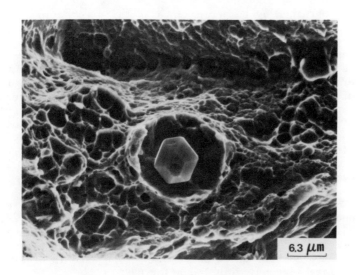

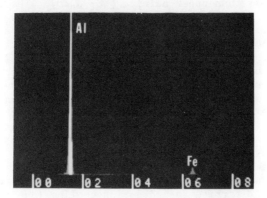

Figure 17.   Scanning electron fractograph showing
an angular inclusion rich in aluminum
in a quenched and tempered 4340+3Al
steel.

This is obtained by tempering in a specific tempering range. Autotempered martensite will exhibit a higher toughness than untempered martensite. The latter is generally in a highly stressed state while, in the former, part of the internal stresses are relieved by the autotempering. However, auto-tempered steels are not as tough as tempered steels. Further relief of both quenching and transformation stresses occurs by tempering at higher temperatures. In addition to stress relief which occurs at higher tempering temperatures, the accompanying precipitation of different types of carbides can drastically alter the strength and toughness. The effect of these carbides on toughness will be discussed in detail in a later section.

Several investigators have shown that the presence of twinned or plate martensite deteriorates toughness [21,22,24, 25,63]. Twinned martensite can be avoided by controlling the composition and M_s temperature. In general, it is recommended that a C content below about 0.4 pct be used in order to avoid plate martensite in low alloy UHSS.

Lower bainite exhibits better combinations of strength and toughness than upper bainite [88-93,25]. The lower tough-ness of the upper bainite is generally attributed to the presence of brittle interlath films of cementite at the fer-rite lath boundaries. It has been suggested that in steels with a carbon content greater than about 0.4 pct lower bainitic structures have a potential for strength-toughness combina-tions better than those that would be obtained in tempered martensite structures [94,19,20,25]. This observation is probably related to the fact that at these higher C levels, twinned martensite of a lower toughness is obtained. How-ever, obtaining a 100% lower bainite structure in the higher C steels may not be commercially feasible.

Ferrite in the matrix structure, either that coexisting with the austenite at the austenitization temperature or the proeuctectoid ferrite formed during cooling (due to low hard-enability), is an undesirable microstructural constituent because it lowers both strength and toughness. The ferrite is a soft phase which can tear easily and lead to early cleavage and fracture [84].

B. Role of Retained Austenite

Retained austenite in UHSS can be beneficial or detri-mental to ductility and toughness depending on its amount, morphology, and stability. As pointed out in an earlier section, retained austenite in UHSS is found in the form of

thin films at the lath boundaries as shown in Figure 12.
Several investigators have shown that these films improve
toughness if they have good thermal and mechanical stability,
i.e. if they do not transform upon tempering and are stable
to the application of stress/strain [63,26-36].

Table IV. Volume Fraction of Retained Austenite in Heat Treated Ultra High Strength Steel

Heat Treatment	Example of Steel	Retained Austenite
Quenched & tempered	4340, 300M	≈ 5 pct
Isothermally Trans- formed	4330+Si, 4340+Al+Si	8-20 pct
Continuously Cooled	300M	6-30 pct

The volume fraction of austenite that can be retained
is a function of composition and temperature. Table IV
shows typical amounts of austenite retained following different heat treatment cycles. Non-carbide forming elements
in steel such as Si and Al, and austenite stabilizers such
as Ni and Mn, can increase the amount of austenite retained
following heat treatment. The effects on mechanical properties,
of changing the amount of austenite in AISI 4340 steels by
Si additions, are shown in Table V. It is seen that at similar strength levels, the ductility was improved by the presence of large amounts of austenite. Too much austenite,
however, can lower strength [65].

If the austenite is thermally unstable and forms carbide
films at the lath boundaries as a result of tempering, the
toughness can be severely degraded [63,29-36]. This effect
has been shown by many investigators in a wide variety of
steels. Garrison [35] studied a silicon modified secondary
hardening steel in which the hardness could be kept fairly
constant following tempering over a range of temperatures
from 200-500°C. The variation in fracture and impact toughness and hardness as a function of tempering temperature for
the experimental steel is shown in Figure 18.

Table V. Mechanical Properties of 4340 Steels Modified With Silicon*

Silicon Content (wt.pct)	Retained Austenite (vol. pct)	0.2 pct Yield Strength MPa (Ksi)	Ultimate Strength MPa (Ksi)	Elongation Pct
1	7	1371 (199)	1571 (228)	6.5
2	13	1406 (204)	1633 (237)	8.7
3	16	1378 (200)	1633 (237)	13.0

* The specimens were austeniteized at 900°C (1hr), isothermally transformed at 300°C (1hr) and air cooled to room temperature. Tempered at 350°C (1hr) and air cooled to room temperature.

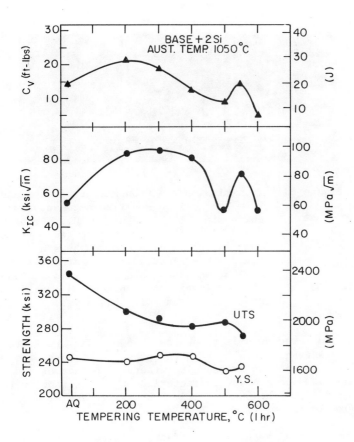

Figure 18.   Variation in yield and ultimate strengths,
plane strain fracture toughness and Charpy
V-notch impact toughness with tempering
temperature for a silicon modified, secondary hardening steel.

A study of the microstructures following tempering at various
temperatures showed that the steep drop in toughness following tempering at 500°C was due to the extensive interlath
precipitation of carbides as shown in Figure 19. In addition,
the austenite which remained following tempering was shown
to be very unstable to the application of stress/strain.
The recovery in toughness following tempering at 550°C was
attributed to the spheroidization of the interlath carbide

films as shown in Figure 20 [79].

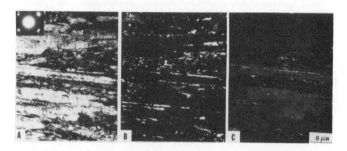

Figure 19.   Transmission electron micrographs obtained
from the silicon modified secondary hardening steel tempered at 500°C. The bright
field picture A shows dislocated martensite,
some intralath carbides, B shows a dark
field of retained austenite at the lath
boundaries and C is a dark field picture
showing interlath carbides and carbides
precipitated on twin boundaries.

The second large drop in toughness at 600°C was attributed to
an alloy segregation effect in the presence of Si at the prior
austenite grain boundaries. The fracture surface of the 500
°C tempered specimen was characterized by transgranular failure and that of the 600°C specimen by intergranular decohesion
as shown in Figure 21.

The mechanical stability of the retained austenite determines the amount of austenite that is transformed to martensite upon the application of stress and strain. If the steel
is unstable to the application of stress a lower yield strength
is observed [95,96]. However, if the retained austenite is
stable to stress and can withstand a certain amount of plastic
strain, it can provide a crack blunting as well as a TRIP
(Transformation Induced Plasticity) effect [28,33,65,96,97].
The effect of mechanical stability on the fracture toughness
has been extensively investigated for TRIP steels wherein the
starting microstructure is fully austenitic [95,96,98-100].
Much less work has been devoted, however, to studying the effects of the mechanical stability of retained austenite in
UHSS [99,28-30]. This is because it is not generally possible
to isolate the effects of the mechanical stability of austenite on toughness.

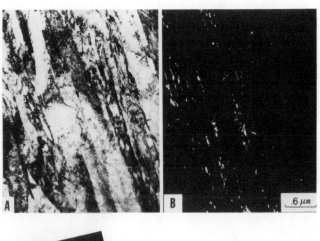

Figure 20. Transmission electron micrographs obtained
from the same steel as in Figure 18 and 20,
but tempered at 550°C. The dark field
picture B was obtained using a cementite
reflection. Note that most of the cementite particles at the lath boundaries are
spheroidized.

Horn [29] investigated the effect of large amounts of
retained austenite in 300 M steel when subjected to slow cooling treatments from the austenitizing temperature. The variation in austenite as a function of temperature and strain
is shown in Figure 22 for the case which simulates air cooling
in a 10 cm thick plate. The retained austenite content was
measured with a magnetic saturation device in the as-cooled
condition and at 2% tensile strain. In the as-cooled state
the austenite was found to be mechanically very unstable.

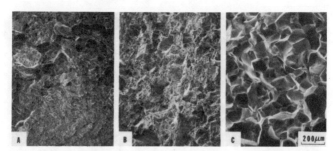

Figure 21. Scanning electron fractographs of the same
steel as in Figure 20. A was obtained from
the fracture surface of a charpy bar tempered at 500°C, B from the specimen tempered
at 550°C, and C was from the 600°C temper
specimen.

The stability of the austenite increased upon tempering up to
350°C and decreased at higher tempering temperatures. The
mechanical properties are presented in Table VI from which
the role of mechanical stability on toughness can be evaluat-
ed. Although the changes in properties are also a result of
other changes in the structure of the steel upon tempering,
definite trends can be observed. For example, the effect of
unstable austenite on the yield strength is clearly observed.
The yield strengths of both the as-cooled and the 450°C
temper specimens are lower and their ultimate tensile strengths
are higher than that of the 300°C temper specimen. As mentioned earlier the lower yield strength can be attributed to the
transformation of the unstable austenite.

A comparison of the toughness data shows that both the
fracture and impact toughness of the 300°C temper specimen
are higher than those of the as-cooled and 450°C temper specimens. Horn [29] reported that there were no significant microstructural differences between the as-cooled and 300°C temper
specimens. The matrix structure was bainite with retained
austenite at the lath boundaries. The only microstructural
feature that is different between the two treatments is the
presence of austenite of different mechanical stability. The
lower stability of the austenite in the as-cooled structure
permitted it to transform rapidly to high carbon brittle
martensite which lowered the toughness. The larger drop in
toughness observed in the 470°C temper specimen has been attributed to the combined effect of thermal destabilization
leading to formation of carbide films upon tempering and
mechanical unstability of the remaining austenite [29,32].

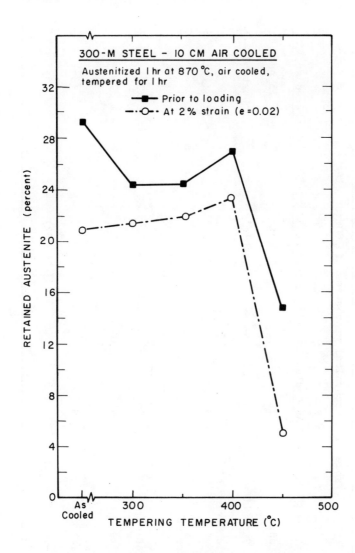

Figure 22.   Variation in retained austenite content
with tempering temperature for a 300 M
steel specimen cooled at a rate which
simulates the air cooling of a 10 cm thick
plate.   The austenite contents were measured prior to loading and at 2% strain with
a magnetic saturation device.

Table VI. Mechanical Properties of 300M Steel*

	As Cooled	Tempered at 300°C	Tempered at 450°C
Austenite Content	29 pct	23 pct	15 pct
Mechanical Stability	'Unstable'	'Stable'	'Unstable'
0.2pct Yield Strength MPa (KSI)	923 (134)	1137 (165)	972 (141)
Tensile Strength MPa (KSI)	1461 (212)	1350 (196)	1557 (226)
Pct. Elongation	16	18	15
Pct. Red. Area	45	55	37
K_{IC} (MPa $\sqrt{m}$) (KSI $\sqrt{in}$)	88 (80)	110 (100)	40 (36)
C_v J (ft-lbs)	34 (25)	44 (32)	7 (5)

* The steel was heat treated to simulate air cooling in a 10 cm thick plate.

Refrigeration experiments might clarify further the effects
of the presence of mechanically unstable austenite on toughness.

One other factor that determines the severity of the
loss of toughness due to thermal and mechanical destabilization of austenite is the carbon content of the retained austenite. In quenched and tempered steels the retained austenite is not generally enriched in carbon whereas in isothermally transformed or slowly cooled steels the austenite retained is so enriched [28]. The carbon content in the retained
austenite determines the thickness and extent of interlath
carbide precipitation that occurs on thermal destabilization
and the carbon content of the martensite which forms due to
mechanical destabilization. Obviously carbon enrichment of
austenite will lead to more interlath precipitation of carbides and/or high carbon brittle martensite and, in turn, to
poor toughness. Thus, the severity of embrittlement which
occurs in quenched and tempered steel is much less than that
observed in isothermally transformed and slowly cooled steels
[28-30].

From the above discussion it is clear that the role of
retained austenite in the fracture of UHSS is complex and
that it is a microstructural feature which needs careful control.

C.   Role of Second Phase Particles

Second phases in UHSS may be present either as precipitates (e.g. carbides, nitrides, intermetallic compounds etc.)
or as inclusions (e.g. oxides and sulfides). In general, inclusions are large compared to precipitates and do not often
provide strengthening of the matrix. Undissolved carbides
can also be large and they seldom provide matrix strengthening. However, undissolved carbides keep carbon out of solution and hence do not allow the steel to achieve its potential strength upon quenching. Both inclusions and undissolved
carbides can alter the toughness of the steel considerably.
When the carbides precipitate within the matrix, i.e. as
intralath carbides, they increase the strength significantly.
However, when the carbides precipitate at the lath and grain
boundaries their major effect is to reduce toughness.

In UHSS it has been easier to understand the role of
inclusions and undissolved carbides on toughness. However,
it is difficult to assess the role of the different types of
intralath carbides on toughness because, inevitably, the pre-

cipitation of these carbides is accompanied by other changes
in structure such as the decomposition of retained austenite
into interlath carbide and ferrite. Interlath carbides, un-
like the intralath carbides, have been shown to have significant effects on toughness depending upon their length and
thickness.

The second-phase parameters which control the ductility
and toughness of steel are (a) volume fraction (b) size,
(c) distribution, (d) hardness, (e) toughness, (f)
bonding to matrix, and (g) shape [101]. In addition to
these parameters, the toughness of steels strengthened by
precipitates is also affected by the crystal structure, co-
herency of the precipitates with the matrix, and the sites
where precipitation occurs. Most studies in UHSS that have
dealt with these parameters have been devoted to inclusions
and large undissolved carbides [2,16,34,102-105]. Far less
work has been done with respect to intralath carbides for
reasons previously mentioned.

Increasing the volume fraction f and size of particles
in a ductile matrix decreases ductility and toughness [106].
For a given volume fraction the size of the particle d determines the interparticle spacing L. Priest [107] has shown
that K_{IC} is proportional to $\sqrt{L}$ at a given strength. The
relationship between f, d and L is given by [106]:

$$L = d \sqrt{\left(\frac{2}{3f}\right)} (1-f)$$

Hence, in order to increase K_{IC}, it is necessary to keep the
interparticle spacing L as large as possible. This can be
achieved by reducing the volume fraction f, and/or increasing
the particle size, d. However, it is not desirable to increase L by increasing d because it has been observed that
the plastic strain necessary to fracture a particle decreases
with increasing particle size [3,104]. Also, the stress required to crack a particle is inversely proportional to the
square root of the particle radius [101]. Therefore, the
finest possible particle size is desirable. The particle
size determines the onset of void formation and the interparticle distance controls void growth. Cox [108] has shown
that an increase in K_{IC} is possible, at constant volume fraction, by reducing both d and L. Apparently the increase in
K_{IC} due to reduced particle size was larger than the decrease
in K_{IC} due to smaller L. Maraging steels usually have much
higher fracture toughness than quenched and tempered steels

at a given strength level. Cox and Low [104] suggested that
the main reason for this difference is that in the low alloy
UHSS voids initiate at inclusions and link-up via sheets of
small voids nucleated at the carbide particles, but in maraging steels only the large voids occur at the Ti(CN) inclusions
and these have to grow until they coalesce. Pellissier [16]
suggested that the high fracture toughness of maraging steels
is a consequence of fine, homogeneously distributed particles
of intermetallic compounds while the low alloy UHSS of similar strength contain larger carbides detrimental to toughness. Roesch and Henry [109], and Psioda and Low [110] observed that in maraging steel dimples can occur at both inclusions and precipitates at high strengths. They reported
that, for voids to occur at precipitates, they must grow
beyond a critical size of 200 Å. However, the critical size
was found to be a function of test temperature; it decreases
with decreasing test temperature.

The conclusion that may be stated is that fine coherent
of semicoherent intralath carbides in UHSS improve strength
and toughness. For example, the precipitation of semicoherent ε carbides in low alloy UHSS such as AISI 4340 can
result in a slight increase in strength and a large increase
in toughness. However, a part of the increase in toughness
that is observed may result from reduction in internal stresses in highly strained brittle as-quenched martensite.

Also it has been shown by Speich et al that in a 10Ni-
Cr-Mo-Co secondary hardening UHSS, maximum toughness is obtained at high strength when coarse Fe_3C precipitates are
replaced by a fine dispersion of alloy carbide [111].

The effects of undissolved primary carbides on toughness
are better known than those due to the carbides precipitated
upon tempering. Undissolved carbides in UHSS lead to a deterioration in toughness. The work of Tom has shown that
there is a threshold size for undissolved carbides above which
the fracture toughness abruptly decreases at a given strength
level [105]. Carlson et.al. associate the increase in K_{IC}
with austenitizing temperature to the dissolution of undissolved carbides [34]. Recent studies by Lechtenberg of two steels,
one containing large undissolved carbides and the other only
fine undissolved carbides, showed that the large undissolved
carbides reduce both the fracture toughness and the impact
toughness at the same strength level [112]. The microstructures of these two steels are shown in Figure 23 from
which it is clearly seen that alloy B1 has large undissolved
carbides and alloy B4 has only fine undissolved carbides.
The variation in fracture toughness with tempering temperature

for these two steels is shown in Figure 24.

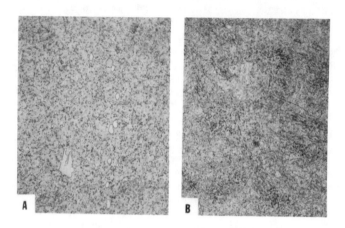

Figure 23.   Optical micrographs of steels (A) B1 and
(B) B4, both austenitized at 1000°C and
oil quenched. Steel B1 has large undissolved carbides whereas steel B4 has only
fine undissolved carbides.

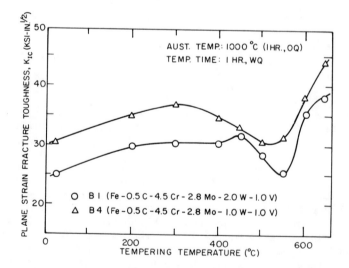

Figure 24.   Variation in plane strain fracture toughness
of steels B1 and B4 with tempering temperature. Note that alloy B4 which has no large
undissolved carbides has higher fracture
toughness than B4 at all tempering temperatures.

It has been reported by Hahn et.al. that at constant volume fraction, the ductility is better when nonbrittle particles and particles which have a better bonding to the matrix are present [113]. Better bonding between the particle and matrix makes it difficult to introduce an interfacial crack. It has been shown that sulfides are more detrimental to ductility than carbides [114]. The reasons for this are probably related to the low hardness and easy deformability of sulfides as compared to carbides.

The shape of second phase particles control not only the strength but also the ductility and toughness. For example, Gladman et.al. have shown that, at a similar volume fraction, the plate morphologies both for sulfides and carbides gave poorer ductilities relative to more equiaxial morphologies, e.g. spheroids [114]. The reasons for this observed behavior can be attributed to a number of factors It is easier to crack particles which are plate or rod-shaped as compared to spherical particles. If interface decohesion between the particle and matrix occurs, it will lead to a larger crack in the case of a plate- or rod-shaped precipitate as compared to a spherical precipitate. Also, Kelly has shown that the strengthening due to rod-shaped particles is 1.7 times, and that due to plate-shpaed particles is about 2 times the strengthening obtained by spherical particles at a particular volume fraction and dislocation density [115]. It has also been shown that K_{IC} decreases as the yield strength increases [86]. All of the above factors can account for the decreased toughness observed in the presence of plate- or rod-shaped precipitates.

The precipitation of cementite in steels generally results in a loss of strength and toughness [42]. The loss in strength occurs because of the rapid loss of C from solution in the martensite and the rapid growth rate of cementite. However, the loss in toughness has been shown to be a result of the formation of interlath carbides--a product of the decomposition of the retained austenite films located at the lath boundaries and due to mechanical instability of the remaining austenite [116,63,29-36].

Investigators in the past have associated embrittlement in the secondary hardening range with the pinning of dislocation intersections by non-coherent particles [117], the re-solution of iron carbides and the subsequent precipitation of alloy carbides which is accompanied by the generation of high dislocation densities [13,14], and the locking of dislocation intersections and jogs by the precipitates [13,14].

However, more recent studies indicate that the embrittlement
observed in UHSS may be due to the formation of interlath carbide networks and in some instances grain boundary segregation
effects [35,79]. When embrittlement is caused by interlath
carbide films, the fracture is usually transgranular as was
shown in Figure 23, but when the embrittlement is caused by
segregation of alloying and impurity elements the fracture
occurs as a result of grain boundary decohesion.

D. Role of Grain Size

When a steel is cooled down from the austenite region,
the austenite grain boundaries provide heterogeneous sites
for nucleation and growth types of transformation products
such as ferrite, bainite, etc. and hence, control hardenability
of the steel. The grain boundaries also limit the size of
the martensite packets which are formed upon quenching. Thus,
although the austenite grain boundaries are not really grain
boundaries following transformation, they affect the size
and nature of the microstructural units which are formed at
lower temperatures. In addition, they provide sites for segregation of alloy and impurity elements during austenitization.
Hence, the prior austenite grain boundaries affect toughness
both directly and indirectly.

The influence of austenitization at temperatures higher than
those conventionally used on the toughness of a wide variety
of steels has been studied by several investigators [26,27,
34,81,105,118-125]. Both the low alloy ultra-high strength
steels (such as 300M, 4340, 4130) and experimental steels
(such as Fe/Cr/C, Cr-Ni-Mn, Fe-Mo-C-Ni steels) have been
studied. These steels had a higher fracture toughness (K_{IC})
when austenitized at higher temperatures as shown in Table
VII. There was no significant change in strength for the low
alloy steels. The medium alloy content steels containing
secondary carbide formers had higher strengths following
austenitization at higher temperatures because of the dissolution of carbides. The higher temperature austenitization
did not provide a corresponding improvement in impact toughness except in the case of the 4330 and 4130 steels [121].
In all these steels there was an increase in grain size with
increasing austenitization temperature.

The improvements in fracture toughness with higher austenitization temperatures were attributed to the presence or absence of various microstructural features. Wood attributed
the improvement in K_{IC} in 4330 and 4130 steel to the prevention of deleterious austenite decomposition such as free

Table VII. Mechanical Properties of Some Ultra High Strength Steels in the As-quenched Condition*

Steel	Aust. Temp. (°C)	0.2pct Y.S MPa	KSI	UTS MPS	KSI	C_v J	ft-lbs	K_{IC} MPA √m	KSIv/in
4130	870	1385	(201)	1957	(284)	9.5	(7.0)	58.8	(53.5)
	1200	1413	(205)	1902	(276)	10.2	(7.5)	95.1	(86.5)
4330	870	1612	(234)	1950	(283)	16.5	(12.1)	69.9	(63.6)
	1200	1440	(209)	1950	(283)	25.6	(18.8)	96.2	(87.5)
4340	870	1633	(237)	2226	(323)	9.3	(6.8)	37.5	(34.1)
	1200	1516	(220)	2246	(326)	7.6	(5.6)	66.4	(58.6)
300 M	870	1537	(223)	2370	(344)	8.6	(6.3)	25.6	(23.3)
	1200	1468	(213)	2301	(334)	6.7	(4.9)	46.6	(42.4)
Fe-0.3C-5Mo	870	1323	(192)	1585	(230)	–	–	57.1	(52.0)
	1200	1447	(210)	1791	(260)	–	–	110.0	(100.00)

* Data from References 105,121.

ferrite and upper bainite in the coarser grain structure [120, 121]. It was suggested that the larger grain size improved hardenability. Lai reported that the improvements in K_{IC} in 4130 steel austenitized at 1200°C could also be attributed to the occurence of autotempering, the presence of interlath austenite films, and the absence of substructural twinning in the martensite [27]. The improvement in K_{IC} with increasing austenitization temperatures in 4340 steel was attributed by Lai et. al. to an increase in the amount of retained austenite and the elimination of twinned martensite [26] whereas the improvement in toughness in Fe-Cr-C steels was attributed to the reduction in size and volume fraction of undissolved carbides by Carlson et.al [34]. A similar explanation for the improvement in toughness of Fe-Mo-C secondary hardening steels had also been proposed by Tom who reported that there was a critical size of undissolved carbides above which the fracture toughness deteriorated significantly [105].

In order to explain the observed effect of an increase in fracture toughness accompanied by a decrease in impact toughness, with increasing austenitization temperature, Ritchie et.al. proposed a model which takes into consideration the basic differences between the K_{IC} and Charpy V notch tests [124]. They showed that in 4340 steel the increased characteristic distance available with larger prior austenite grain sizes would result in superior values of toughness in the presence of a sharp notch (as used in K_{IC} tests) and low values of toughness in the presence of a blunt notch (as used in the Charpy test). Ritchie and Horn reported that the increase in K_{IC} (for sharp cracks), for failure by fibrous fracture in 4340 steel, was associated with the large characteristic distance resulting from dissolution of void initiating particles at high austenitizing temperatures [125]. They also suggested that the presence of retained austenite film is not an important microstructural feature affecting toughness changes due to variations in austenitizing temperature.

Several investigators have noted that the severity of tempered martensite embrittlement obtained in steels austenitized at higher temperatures is greater than that obtained in the steels austenitized at conventional temperatures. Ritchie et.al. suggested that the larger grain size developed at the higher austenitization temperatures markedly increases the effect of any impurity-induced grain boundary embrittlement [81].

Recent investigations in low carbon structural steels tested at cryogenic temperatures revealed that K_{IC} increases with a decrease in prior austenite grain size [126]. It was

also observed that when the plastic zone size at the crack
tip was very small, as was the case at very low temperatures,
the fracture toughness was independent of grain size. The
mode of fracture at these temperatures was generally cleavage.
It is also well established that the ductile to brittle transition temperature is lowered by grain refinement [127].

The above discussion reveals the complex nature of the
effects of prior austenite grain size on toughness. The prior
austenite grain size can also influence other properties of
importance in steels. For example, it has been shown that
larger grain size results in increased resistance to environ-
mentally assisted fracture in both sustained loading hydrogen-
induced cracking and in near-threshold crack propagation tests
[128,129]. Thus, it appears that to obtain the optimum combination of properties, ultra-high strength steels should be
austenitized at the lowest possible temperature that will
minimize deleterious microstructural features such as ferrite,
large undissolved carbides, upper bainite and twinned martensite and will provide a reasonable prior austenite grain size.

SUMMARY

The mechanical properties of steel especially strength
and toughness are controlled by various factors such as melting technique, hotworking practice, thermomechanical processing, environment and microstructure. The role of microstructure
as affected by composition and heat treatment in the fracture
of ultra high strength steels was presented within this paper.

The fine scale microstructural features usually found in
ultra high strength steels were described. It was concluded
that microconstituents such as twinned martensite, large undissolved carbides, interlath carbides, nonmetallic inclusions
and free ferrite were detrimental to toughness. The complex
role of retained austenite and grain size was discussed in
detail. Microstructures containing lath martensite, fine
intralath carbides, retained austenite of the right morphology
and stability obtained by austenitizing at optimal austenitization temperatures generally provide the best combinations
of strength and toughness.

ACKNOWLEDGEMENTS

The work discussed above was a summary of investigations conducted during the past decade by several postdoctural and graduate students at Berkeley. The lively discussions we have had with our mentor Professor Earl Parker and colleagues Drs. Goolsby, Lai, Wood, Tom, Bhandarkar, Babu, Ritchie, Horn, Kohn, Rao, Garrison, Lechtenberg, Kar and others have been invaluable. We would like to thank them all for their contributions. We are very grateful to Mr. Paul Spencer and Dr. Yoshi Mishima for their patience and help in preparing this manuscript.

This work was funded by the U.S. Department of Energy.

REFERENCES

1. "Introduction to Todays Ultra-High Strength Structural Steels". A.M. Hall, ASTM - STP 498, American Society for Testing and Materials, Philadelphia, PA. 19103, 1971.

2. George E. Gazza, and Frank R. Larson, Trans. ASM, 58, 1965, p 183.

3. T.B. Cox and J.R. Low, Jr., Met. Trans., 5, 1974, p 1457.

4. M.K. Koul, Met. Eng. Quart., February 1976, p 1.

5. D.J. Latham, JISI, 1970, p 50.

6. V.F. Zackay, Mat. Sci. and Eng. 25, 1976, p 247.

7. J.M. Capus and G. Mayer, Metallurgia, 62, 1960, p 133.

8. C.J. McMahan, ASTM-STP 407, American Society for Testing and Materials, Philadelphia, PA 19103, 1968, p 127.

9. D.F. Stein, Ann. Rev. Mater. Sci., 7, 1977, p 123.

10. B.S. Lement, B.L. Averbach, and M. Cohen, Trans., ASM, 46, 1954, p 851.

11. B.G. Residorf, Trans. AIME, 227, 1963, p 1334.

12. A.J. Baker, F.S. Lauta, and R.P. Wei, "Structure and Properties of Ultra High Strength Steels", ASTM-STP 370, American Society for Testing and Materials, Philadelphia, PA. 19103, 1965, p 3.

13. Bani R. Banerjee, idem. p 94.

14. Bani R. Banerjee, JISI, 203, 1965, p 166.

15. J.H. Bucher, G.W. Powell and J.W. Spretenak, Met. Soc. AIME Conference Series, Vol. 31, Gordon and Breach Science Publ., New York, 1966, p 323.

16. G.E. Pellissier, Eng. Frac. Mech., 1, 1968, p 55.

17. E.B. Kula and A.A. Anctil, J. Mater., 4 (4), 1969, p 817.

18. D.E. Hodgson and A.S. Tetelman, Proc. 2nd Intern Conf. Fracture, Chapman and Hall, London, 1969, p 253.

19. Y.H. Liu, Trans. ASM, 62, 1969, p 55.

20. Y.H. Liu, Trans. ASM, 62, 1969, p 545.

21. S.K. Das and G. Thomas, Trans. ASM 62, 1969, p 659.

22. Der-Hung Huang and G. Thomas, Met. Trans., 2, 1971, p 1587.

23. Roger D. Goolsby, Ph.D. Thesis, LBL-405, University of California, Lawrence Berkeley Laboratory, Berkeley, California 94720, 1971.

24. M. Raghavan and G. Thomas, Met. Trans., 2, 1971, p 3433.

25. G. Thomas, Iron and Steel International, October 1973, p 451.

26. G.Y. Lai, W.E. Wood, R.A. Clark, V.F. Zackay and E.R. Parker, Met. Trans., 5, 1974, p 1663.

27. G.Y. Lai, Mat. Sci, and Eng., 19, 1975, p 153.

28. G. Kohn, Ph.D. Thesis, LBL-5716, University of California, Lawrence Berkeley Laboratory, Berkeley, California 94720, 1976.

29. R. Horn, Ph.D. Thesis, LBL-5787, University of California, Lawrence Berkeley Laboratory, Berkeley, California 94720, 1976.

30. M.S. Bhat, Ph.D. Thesis, LBL-6046, University of California, Lawrence Berkeley Laboratory, Berkeley, California 94720 1977.

31. G. Thomas, Met. Trans. A., 9A, 1978, p 439.

32. R.M. Horn and R.O. Ritchie, Met. Trans. A, 9A, 1978, p 1039.

33. B.V.N. Rao, Ph.D. Thesis, LBL-7361, University of California, Lawrence Berkeley Laboratory, Berkeley, California 94720, 1978.

34. M.F. Carlson, B.V.N. Rao, and G. Thomas, Met. Trans. A., 10A, 1979, p 1273.

35. W.M. Garrison, Jr. Ph.D. Thesis, University of California, Berkeley, California 94720, 1980.

36. B.V.N. Rao and G. Thomas, Met. Trans. A., 11A, 1980, p 441.

37. P.M. Kelly and J. Nutting, JISI, 206, 1967, p 385.

38. G. Krauss and A.R. Marder, Met. Trans., 2, 1971, p 2343.

39. G. Thomas, Met. Trans., 2, 1971, p 2373.

40. E.W. Page, P. Manganon, Jr., G. Thomas, and V.F. Zackay, Trans. ASM., 62, 1969, p 45.

41. E.C. Bain and H.W. Paxton, Alloying Elements in Steel, American Society for Metals, Ohio, 1966, p 182.

42. G.R. Speich and W.C. Leslie, Met. Trans., 3, 1972, 1043.

43. R.W.K. Honeycombe, "Structure and Strength of Alloy Steels", Climax Molybdenum Company.

44. A. Kasak, V.K. Chandhok and E.J. Dulis, Trans. ASM, 56, 1963, p 455.

45. M.G.H. Wells, Acta. Met. 12, 1964, p 389.

46. D. Huang and G. Thomas, Met. Trans. A., 8A, 1977, p 1661.

47. W.S. Owen, JISI, 177, 1954, p 445.

48. H.W. King and S.G. Glover, JISI, 196, 1960, p 281.

49. A.S. Kenneford and T. Williams, JISI, 196, 1960, p 281.

50. E. Tekin and P.M. Kelly, Precipitation from Iron-Base Alloys, Vol. 28, Met. Soc. of AIME Conference Series, Eds. B. Gilbert, R. Speich, and J.B. Clark, Gordon and Breach Science Publ., New York, 1965, p 173.

51. W.C. Leslie, R.M. Fisher, and N. Sen, Acta. Met., 7, 1959, p 632.

52. K.H. Jack, JISI, 169, 1951, p 26.

53. W.C. Leslie, Acta. Met., 9, 1961, p 1004.

54. V. Krasevec, M. Macek, and J. Rodic, Acta. Met., 28, 1980, p 223.

55. D.N. Shackelton and P.M. Kelly, Physical Properties of Martensite and Bainite, ISI Spec. Report 93, Iron and Steel Institute, London, 1965, p 126.

56. R.W.K.Honeycombe and F.B. Pickering, Met. Trans., 3, 1972, p 1099.

57. R.F. Heheman, K.R. Kinsman and H.I. Aaronson, Met. Trans., 3, 1972, p 1077.

58. Der-Hung Huang, Ph.D. Thesis, LBL-3713, University of California, Lawrence Berkeley Laboratory, Berkeley, California 94720.

59. M. Cohen, Trans. ASM, 41, 1949, p 35.

60. B.L. Averbach and M. Cohen, Trans. ASM, 41, 1949, p 1024.

61. L.C. Castleman, B.L. Averbach, and M. Cohen, Trans. ASM, 44, 1952, p 263.

62. C.J. Altstetter, M. Cohen, and B.L. Averbach, Trans. ASM 55, 1962, p 287.

63. J. McMahon and G. Thomas, Proc. Third Intern. Conf. on Strength of Metals and Alloys, Inst. of Metals, London, 1973, 1, p 180.

64. B.V.N. Rao, J.Y. Koo, and G. Thomas, EMSA Proceedings, Claitor Publishing Division, Baton Rouge, 1975, p 30.

65. D. Webster, Trans. ASM, 61, 1968, p 816.

66. B.N.P. Babu, Ph.D. Thesis, LBL-2772, University of California, Lawrence Berkeley Laboratory, Berkeley, California 94720, 1974.

67. Transformations in Metals, Paul G. Shewmon, McGraw Hill Book Company, New York, 1969, p 338.

68. W.C. Leslie and R.L. Miller, Trans. ASM, 57, 1964, p 972.

69. H.R. Woehrle, W.R. Clough, and G.S. Ansell, Trans. ASM, 59, 1966, p 784.

70. A.R. Troiano, Trans. ASM, 41, 1949, p 1093.

71. J.A. Cameron, JISI, July 1956, p 260.

72. E.P. Kleir and A.R. Troiano, Metals Technology, 12, 1945, p 1.

73. G.S. Ansell, S.J. Donachie and R.W. Messler, Jr., Met. Trans., 2, 1971, p 2443.

74. B. Edmondson and T. Ko, Acta Met., 2, 1954, p 235.

75. P.M. Kelly and J. Nutting, JISI, 197, 1961, p 199.

76. J.H. Woodhead and A.G. Quarrell, "The Role of Carbides in Low-Alloy Creep Resisting STeels", Climax Molybdenum Company, 2 Cavendish Place, London, WI, England.

77. A. Westgren, G. Phragmen and T.N. Negresco, JISI, 117, 1928, p 383.

78. H.J. Goldschmidt, JISI, 160, 1948, p 345.

79. M.S. Bhat, W.M. Garrison, Jr. and V.F. Zackay, Mat. Sci. and Eng., 41, 1979, p 1.

80. G.Y. Lai, W.E. Wood, E.R. Parker, and V.F. Zackay, "Influence of Microstructural Features on Fracture Toughness of an Ultra-high Strength Steel", LBL-2236, Lawrence Berkeley Laboratory, Berkeley, CA 94720.

81. G. Clark, R.O. Ritchie and J.F. Knott, Nat. Phys. Sci., 239, 1972, p 104.

82. H.W. McQuaid, Trans. ASM, 23, 1935, p 797.

83. D. Hall and G.H.J. Bennett, JISI, 205, 1967, p 309.

84. V.F. Zackay and E.R. Parker, Alloy Design, ed. John K. Tien and George S. Ansell, Academic Press.

85. A.R. Rosenfeld and A.J. McEvily, AGARD Report, "Metallurgical Aspects of Fatigue and Fracture Toughness", December 1973, p 23.

86. Karl Heinz Schwalbe, Eng. Frac. Mech., 9, 1977, p 795.

87. R.J.H. Wanhill, Eng. Frac. Mech., 10, 1978, p 337.

88. K.J. Irvine and F.B Pickering, JISI, 201, 1963, p 518.

89. F.B. Pickering, Proc. Eng. Reg. Conf. on Elect. Micr., Delft. 1, 1969, p 477.

90. F.B. Pickering, "Metallurgical Achievements", Pergamon Press, 1965, p 109.

91. F.B. Pickering, "Transformation and Hardenability in Steels", Climax Molybdenum Company, Ann Arbor, Michigan, 1967, p 69.

92. Physical Metallurgy and the Design of Steels, F.B. Pickering, Applied Science Publishers Ltd, London, 1978, p 115.

93. N.J. Kar, Ph.D. Thesis, University of California, Berkeley, 1979.

94. L.J. Klinger, N.J. Barnett, R.P. Frohmberg and A.R. Troiano, Trans. ASM, 46, 1954, p 1557.

95. D. Fahr, Met. Trans., 2, 1971, p 1883.

96. D. Bhandarkar, V.F. Zackay, and E.R. Parker, Met. Trans., 3, 1972, p 2619.

97. S.D. Antolovich, A. Saxena, and G.R. Chanani, Met. Trans., 5, 1974, p 623.

98. V.F. Zackay, E.R. Parker, D. Fahr, and R. Bush, Trans. ASM, 60, 1967, p 252.

99. V.F. Zackay, M.D. Bhandarkar, and E.R. Parker, Proceedings 21st Sagmore Army Materials Research Conference on Advances in Deformation Processing, Raquette Lake, New York, August, 1974.

100. W.W. Gerberich, G. Thomas, E.R. Parker and V.F. Zackay, Proc. Int. Conference on Strength of Metals and Alloys, Asilomar, California, 1970, p 894.

101. Raymond F. Decker, Met. Trans., 4, 1973, p 2495.

102. A.J. Birkle, R.P. Wei and G.E. Pellissier, Trans. ASM, 59, 1966, p 981.

103. W.A. Spitzig, Trans. ASM, 61, 1974, p 415.

104. T.B. Cox and J.R. Low, Jr., "An Investigation of the Plastic Fracture in High Strength Steels", NASA Tech. Rept. No. 5, Dept. of Metallurgy and Materials Science, Carnegie-Mellon University, Pittsburgh, May 1973.

105. T. Tom, Ph.D. Thesis, LBL-1856, University of California, Lawrence Berkeley Laboratory, Berkeley, California 94720, 1973.

106. B.I. Edelson and W.M. Baldwin, Jr., Trans. ASM, 55, 1962, p 230.

107. A.H. Priest, Discussion Section in "Effect of Second Phase Particles on the Mechanical Properties of Steel", ISI Special Report 145, The Iron and Steel Institute, London, 1971.

108. T.B. Cox, NASA NAR - 39-0870993, Report No. 4296, 1974.

109. L. Roesch and G. Henry, ASTM-STP 381, American Society for Testing and Materials, Philadelphia, 1969.

110. J.A. Psioda and J.R. Low, Jr., NASA TR N06, NASA Grant NGR-39-087-003, 1974.

111. G.R. Speich, D.S. Dabkowski and L.F. Porter, Met. Trans., 4, 1973, p 303.

112. T. Lechtenberg, Ph.D. Thesis, University of California, Berkeley, California, 94720, 1979.

113. G.T. Hahn, M.F. Kanninen and A.R. Rosenfield, Ann. Rev. Mat. Sci. 2, 1972, p 381.

114. T. Gladman, B. Holmes and I.D. McIvor, "Effect of Second Phase Particles on the Mechanical Properties of Steel", ISI Special Report 145, The Iron and Steel Institute, London, 1971.

115. P.M. Kelly, Scripta Met., 6 (8) 1972, p 647.

116. J.P. Materkowski and George Krauss, Met. Trans. A., 10A, 1979, p 1643.

117. C.R. Simcoe and A.E. Nehrenberg, Trans. ASM, 58, 1965, p 378.

118. V.F. Zackay, E.R. Parker, R.D. Goolsby, and W.E. Wood, Nature Phys. Sci., 236, 1972, p 188.

119. R.O. Ritchie and J.F. Knott, Met. Trans., 5, 1974, p 782.

120. W.E. Wood, Eng. Frac. Mech., 1, 1975, p 219.

121. William E. Wood, Earl R. Parker and Victor F. Zackay, LBL-1474, Lawrence Berkeley Laboratory, Berkeley, California, 94720, 1973.

122. J.L. Youngblood and M. Raghavan, Met. Trans A., 8A, 1977, p 1439.

123. D.S. McDarmaid, Met. Tech., 4, 1978, p 7.

124. R.O. Ritchie, B. Francis, and W.L. Server, Met. Trans. A, 7A, 1976, p 831.

125. R.O. Ritchie and R.M. Horn, Met. Trans A., 9A, 1978, p 331.

126. W. Dahl and W. Kretzschmann, "Fracture 1977", University of Waterloo, 2, 1977, p 17.

127. R.W. Armstrong, Advances in Material Research, ed. H. Herman, 4, 1970, p 101.

128. J.F. Lesser and W.W. Gerberich, Met. Trans A., 7A, 1976, p 953.

129. R.O. Ritchie, Met. Sci., 11, 1977, p 368

FRACTURE MECHANISMS AND MICROSTRUCTURAL
INTERRELATIONSHIPS IN Ni-BASE ALLOY SYSTEMS

S.M. Copley

Fatigue and stress-rupture limit the useful life of Ni-base superalloys in many applications. This presentation reviews briefly the initiation and propagation of fracture in these alloys during fatigue and static loading with particular emphasis on fracture mechanisms and microstructural interrelationships.

A nickel-base superalloy may be described as a Ni/Cr solid solution γ, strengthened by addition of Al and Ti to precipitate $Ni_3(Al,Ti)$. The precipitate γ', is ordered FCC with Al and Ti atoms at the corners of the unit cell and Ni atoms at the face centers. Commercial superalloys generally contain Co to raise the solidus temperature of γ', refractory metal additions for solution strengthening and C, B and Zn to promote ductility. The carbon reacts to form a variety of carbon phases (MC, $M_{23}C_6$, M_6C and M_7C_3) depending on composition and heat treatment. The compositions of two representative Ni-base superalloys, Udimet 700 and Mar M200 are given in Table 1.

Nickel-base superalloys can be classified as cast alloys or wrought alloys. Generally wrought superalloys contain less than 35 v/o γ'. Mar M200 is a cast alloy and contains 65 v/o γ'. Udimet 700 contains 35 v/o γ' and is used in both the wrought and cast conditions. Results reported here will be limited to these alloys but are believed to be applicable to other wrought and cast superalloys.

Superalloys deform plastically by the motion of pairs of $a/2 < 110 >$ dislocations.[1] A single $a/2 < 110 >$ dislocation has to create a high energy antiphase boundary if it penetrates a γ' particle. When the pair moves in the γ'

phase the leading dislocation creates APB while the trailing dislocation annihilates it. At the coherent boundary between γ and γ', however, some APB must be produced when the pair enters the particle resulting in an energy barrier. This interaction between pairs of dislocations and the γ' interfaces produces a large athermal contribution to the yield stress of superalloys up to 1500°F.

Pair motion in superalloys results in two important effects from the standpoint of fracture: (1) Slip due to dislocation motion is concentrated in very narrow shear bands because it is difficult for the pairs to cross-slip; (2) The grains are so resistant to plastic deformation that deformation tends to occur by grain boundary sliding. The former effect plays a role in both the initiation and propagation of fatigue cracks. The latter has led to the introduction of carbon into superalloys precipitating $M_{23}C_6$ at grain boundaries to "key" them and thus reduce grain boundary sliding.[2,3] Unfortunately, in the many alloys this results also in the precipitation of MC carbides from the melt which also plays a role in fracture.[4]

In LCF of wrought U700 at room temperature, cracks are initiated at slip bands.[5] In the high strain range regime, many short cracks form in each surface grain at 5-10% of fatigue life. In the low strain range regime, fracture tends to develop from a few slip band cracks, which propagate all the way across the grains. In the temperature range 600 to 1000°F, dynamic strain aging occurs which results in the dispersal of slip.[6] In this temperature range, fracture is initiated at both external and internal coherent twin boundaries. Coherent twin boundaries are also the initiation sites for fractures in HCF of wrought U700 at room temperature.

In cast alloys, such as Mar M200, cracks are initiated at MC carbides.[7] These carbides often contain cracks running parallel to their long dimension, which are believed to arise from compositional variation and to form during growth from the melt. These cracks cause internal slip bands to form at stresses much less than the yield stress which become initiation sites for cracks in the material adjacent to the carbide particles. In cast alloys, pores lead to the formation of intense shear bands that also act as initiation sites for cracks.

In LCF of wrought Udimet 700 at room temperature, the linking up of cracks in surface grains is referred to as Stage I propagation. The resulting fracture surface is crys-

tallographic. As the fracture propagates away from the surface it spreads in the plane perpendicular to the stress axis.
The fracture surface exhibits ductile striations. This behavior is referred to as Stage II propagation and it continues
until stress overload failure takes place. At 600 to 1000°F,
cyclic strain aging impedes slip so that cracks are initiated
at both external and internal coherent twin boundaries. Overload failure eventually occurs through crack growth and link-
up. The HCF behavior is similar, however, fewer cracks are
nucleated.

At high temperatures (T > 1200°F), grain boundary fracture is dominant.[8] Additional factors must be considered
such as frequency, superimposed creep effects and the environment. There is evidence that for fatigue in an active environment, increasing the frequency may decrease the crack
propagation rate and thus extend the fatigue life.[9] There is
also evidence that oxidation may retard crack growth, pos-
sibly by blunting the crack.[10]

Fracture initiation in stress rupture testing of Udimet
700 involves triple point cracking of the type described by
Chang and Grant at high stresses,[11] and cavitation cracking
similar to that occurring in pure metals at low stresses.[12]
Cracks grow along grain boundaries perpendicular to the stress
axes. Vacancy diffusion along grain boundaries to the crack
tip may be an important growth mechanism. In cast superalloys such as Mar M200 cracks are initiated at precracked
MC carbides during stress rupture testing.[4] Concentration
gradients arising from vacancy between grain boundaries perpendicular to and parallel to the stress axis may lead to
morphological instability.[13] The role of this effect on
fracture during stress rupture has not been determined.

TABLE 1
Compositions of Udimet 700 and Mar M200 (wt pct)

Udimet 700		Mar M200	
0.08 C	5.2 Mo	0.15 C	5.0 Al
15.0 Cr	3.5 Ti	9.0 Cr	0.015 B
Bal Ni	4.3 Al	Bal Ni	0.05 Zr
18.5 Co	0.03 B	10.0 Co	12.5 W
		2.0 Ti	1.0 Cb

REFERENCES

(1) S.M. Copley and B.H. Kear, Trans. Met. Soc. AIME 239, 984 (1967).
(2) W. Betteridge and A.W. Franklin, J. Inst. Metals, 85, 473 (1956-57).
(3) C.W. Weaver, Acta Met. 8, 343 (1960).
(4) S.M. Copley, B.H. Kear and F.L. Ver Snyder, "The Role of Interfaces in Ni-Base Superalloys", in Surfaces and Interfaces, Vol. II, Syracuse, N.Y. (1968).
(5) C.H. Wells and C.P Sullivan, Trans. Quart. ASM 57, 841 (1964).
(6) C.H. Wells and C.P. Sullivan, Trans. Quart. ASM 60, 217 (1967).
(7) M. Gell and G.R. Leverant, Trans. Met. Soc. AIME 242, 1869 (1968).
(8) C.H. Wells and C.P. Sullivan, Trans. Quart. ASM 61, 149 (1968).
(9) G.P. Tully, Proc. Inst. Mech. Eng. 180, 1045 (1965-66).
(10) M. Gell and G.R. Leverant, "The Effect of Temperature on Fatigue Fracture in a Directionally Solidified Nickel-Base Superalloy Proceedings, Second International Conference on Fracture (1969).
(11) H.C. Chang and N.J. Grant, Trans. Met. Soc. AIME 206, 544 (1956).
(12) J.N. Greenwood, D.R. Miller, and J.W. Suiter, Acta Met. 2, 250 (1954).
(13) M.N. Menon and S.M. Copley, Acta Met. 23, 199 (1975).

USING FRACTURE SURFACE DEFORMATION MARKINGS TO DETERMINE CRACK PROPAGATION DIRECTIONS

C. D. Beachem
Naval Research Laboratory

The direction of crack propagation in wrought alloys is a must for many failure analyses. Macroscopic fracture surface markings such as chevrons and shear lips and "T" intersections usually suffice in overload cases, and the shapes of instantaneous flaw fronts such as beach marks and periodic overload features usually do the job in fatigue and corrosion fatigue. The rare occasion arises, however, where macroscopic markings are absent or conflicting. In such instances the electron microscopes are useful.

The simple process of precision matching has been used in recent years to study crack tip mechanisms and the process has shown two essential facts (they weren't the facts which were sought at the time, but are nevertheless true): (I) cracks on the microscopic scale usually grow at angles to the local macroscopic direction of the maximum tensile stress, σ_T , and (2) the mating fracture surfaces are not the same - they are not mirror images - one surface is deformed more than its mate. We now know why metallographic cross sections of cracks show edges which don't quite mate up.

One surface is deformed more than its mate because the crack grows at an angle, as shown in Fig. I.(I). The dimples between the arrows in the left hand fractograph in Fig. I(a) are deformed more than their mates to the right. Figure I(b) shows why this is so. The stresses on surface A are substantially reduced but on surface B they have remained high. Surface B is thus deformed more than A either as the crack grows or after the crack tip has passed, or both. Additional precision matching studies have shown that mating dimples usually have different shapes as shown in Fig. I(c). Shear dimples of the same length (left) are rare, and tear dimples of the same length are rare (right). Most microvoid coalescence results from a combination of tensile and shear motions as shown in the middle three diagrams. Fig. I(a) shows equiaxed dimples on one surface which mate with tear dimples on the other, as sketched in Fig. I(c)(c) .

This difference in deformation between the two surfaces has also been seen in fatigue (Fig. 2), and stress corrosion cracking (Fig. 3) (2). Figure 2(a) shows mating fatigue patches in 2024-T3 aluminum alloy, where the crack grew at 34° to the local tensile stress, with the bottom surface being deformed (slip band cracks) more than the top. This is sketched in Fig. 2(b) (left). In stress corrosion cracking, Fig. 3, the higher deformation takes the shape of the one surface containing more cracks than the other (Fig. 3(b), right).

In all three of these examples the surface with the most deformation faces the origin as shown in Fig. I(b). Precision matching is not needed to do the crack propagation direction analyses however. A single fracture surface contains small neighboring regions of different crack growth directions relative to σ_1 , and contain resultant deformation markings.

In summary; (1) cracks usually don't grow straight because they tend to follow planes of maximum shear, (2) the surface facing the crack origin is stretched more and has more damage, and (3) neighboring regions on a single fracture surface provide ample information to do the crack propagation direction analysis.

One needs only to determine which of these regions are the more heavily damaged and see which way it slopes in order to determine the crack propagation direction.

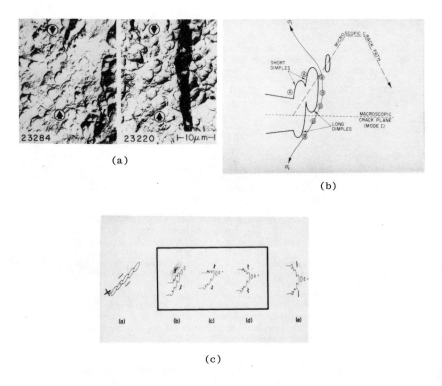

(a)

(b)

(c)

Fig. I. Microvoid coalescence along planes of maximum shear stress. Tear dimples are shown on the left (a) which mate with equiaxed dimples on the right. The state of stress which causes this is shown in (b). The most prevalent modes of microvoid coalescence are the three modes in the center of (c).

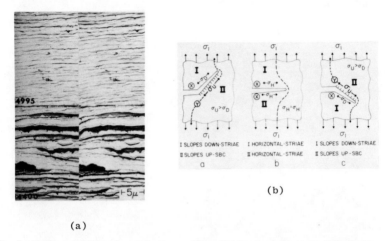

(b)

(a)

Fig. 2. Fatigue striations in an aluminum alloy. Slip band cracks are seen in stereo on the surface which faces the origin (bottom, (a)). This surface was fatigued after the crack tip had passed due to the high stresses remaining on the surface which faces the origin (b).

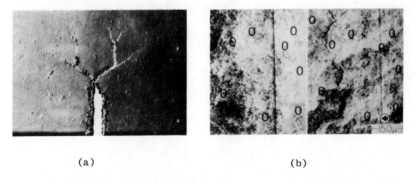

(a)   (b)

Fig. 3. Stress corrosion cracking in steel (a) with the mating surfaces shown in (b). Surface facing the origin is at the right in (b).

REFERENCES

(1).   C. D. Beachem, "The Effects of Crack Tip Plastic Flow Directions Upon Microscopic Dimple Shapes." Met. Trans., Vol. 6A, pp. 377-383, 1975.

(2).   C. D. Beachem, "Microscopic Fatigue Fracture Surface Features in 2024-T3 Aluminum and the Influence of Crack Propagation Angle Upon Their Formation." ASM Transactions, Vol. 60, Sep 1967, pp. 324-343.

PRACTICAL ASPECTS OF THE ENGINEERING
PROBLEM INVESTIGATION

Donald O. Cox
George E. Moller
Failure Analysis Associates
Los Angeles, California

ABSTRACT

The satisfactory solution to an engineering problem requires a balance of investigative know-how, laboratory testing
and engineering analysis. The investigator must determine
the needs of the client, discover the true problem and define
it, gather field and service data, conduct testing as necessary, locate appropriate literature and engineering data, and
perform appropriate analyses to arrive at the optimum solution.

The basic approach employed by Failure Analysis Associates
during the investigation and analysis of numerous engineering
problems is reviewed. A checklist of questions and information to request is presented. The methods employed during an
on-site visit are discussed including the use of the "Failure
Kit". Sources for technical information are discussed and a
proven method for organizing an effective technical library
is presented.

INTRODUCTION

Failures in engineering systems have become much more
costly as the complexity of technology has increased. In
addition to replacement costs and lost production revenues,
there can be the additional expense of product liability
claims which may arise from such instances. The increase in
insurance rates, primarily prompted by the product liability
factor, has caused many companies to self-insure. The cost
of accidents, which in the past were covered by insurance
companies, must now be financed "in-house". Thus, company
management has become even more aware of the value and neces-
sity of properly conducted failure analysis investigations.

119

Only through thorough accurate investigation and analyses
can the true cause(s) and proper remedies for a failure be
established. While each failure investigation is unique,
there is a basic approach which has been shown by past experience to be useful in assessing the failure of a mechanical
system or component. The intent of this paper is to outline
and discuss this methodology. There are a number of references which discuss the failure analysis investigation and
various aspects of the methodology[1-8]. Therefore, only those
aspects which are felt to be unique or need further emphasis
will be discussed here. However, an outline of the approach
employed is included as an Appendix.

PROBLEM DEFINITION

The initial statement of a problem as given by the client
frequently addresses a detail of a major problem. This detail
may have been chosen because of an obvious fracture or as a
result of a cursory analysis previously conducted. This pat-
tern is more likely to occur the greater the amount of time
which has passed since the accident took place. For this
reason it should be emphasized that the failure analyst should
be brought in and exposed to the situation as soon as possible
after the accident takes place.

When the analyst is confronted with a specific problem, it
is imperative that he (she) make the effort to get as much background information regarding the incident as possible. Only
in this way can it be assured that the true nature of the incident has been uncovered, the problem defined correctly, and
the subsequent investigation and analysis will be directed
properly. If the problem is not correctly defined, extensive
work may be performed in an area which may be irrelevant.
Not only is this a waste of time, effort, and the client's
money, but the problem which deserves serious attention may
be missed entirely, leading to the possibility of a similar
failure in the future.

The analyst should also obtain information about the engineering design and legal actions which may be pending. The
history of the subject system or component including all maintenance records should be closely scrutinized. In addition,
the service history of the system or component as a class
should be obtained so that any trends or patterns in behavior
or failure can be studied. This information will also point
to areas which should be checked closely during the investigation. The client can usually provide the information from
knowledge or records.

FIELD INVESTIGATION

If the client employs the services of the failure analyst
as soon as possible after the incident, a trip to the accident
site and examination of the damages can be made before the evidence is altered or lost. Only in this way can the analyst be
totally objective and thorough since this area of his analysis
must otherwise be based on information obtained solely by others.

Prior to the field investigation the analyst should obtain
as much information as is necessary to have a good understanding of how the system and its various components function during operation. This can be obtained through discussions with
knowledgeable personnel or by examination of literature which
discusses the equipment. The analyst should not hesitate to
ask questions if certain aspects of the operation are unclear.
Remember, he (she) is being asked to solve a problem and it is
difficult to do this if the system and operating circumstances
are not fully understood.

The major objectives of the field investigation are (1)
documentation of the damages and observations found at the
accident site, and (2) proper selection of samples for subsequent examination in the laboratory. Primary methods of
documentation are photography, dimensioned sketches, and nara-
tive descriptions.

Extensive photographic documentation is essential. As the
investigation progresses, something which was originally
thought to be insignificant may become important and the photographs taken during the original field investigation may be the
only record available. It is useful to include in the photographs some instrument (usually a scale or measuring tape)
which gives an estimate of the size of the elements photographed. Notes should be made as photographs are taken which
describe what is being photographed and the direction one is
looking (north, inboard, etc.).

Photography is a key element during the on-site investigation and it has been found that a 35 mm camera is optimum for
use in the field. They are easy to handle and operate, are
rugged, and the negative size is large enough that enlarge-
ments can be made without loss of detail. The camera should
be equipped with a 50 or 55 mm macrolens. Such a lens is
capable of taking macrophotos of small pieces or fracture surfaces yet can still be used to take overall photographs. This
eliminates the difficulty associated with the use of extension
tubes or changing from lens to lens. It is also suggested

that a 28 mm wide-angle lens be included in the failure analyst's equipment. While the 50 mm macrolens can be used for most photographs, there are some instances where the wide-angle lens is required to get everything of importance into the field of view.

Dimensional sketches and narrative descriptions should also be made which can later be used with the photographs to complete the documentation. Since sketches take time, they should only be as detailed as necessary to describe the important points and dimensions. The narrative descriptions are important because as time goes by details which may be important may be forgotten. A small portable tape recorder can be useful, as information can be dictated easier and more quickly than written.

During the field investigation, it should become apparent which components, parts, or wreckage will require further analysis in the laboratory. These items should be tagged and their location and condition should be well documented by photography and narrative descriptions prior to removal and transport back to the laboratory.

A "failure analysis kit" is a useful aid in the pursuit of a professional field investigation. This kit is similar to a doctor's medical bag or mechanic's tool box. Tools in the kit can be varied to suit the assignment. Table 1 lists the tools and paraphenalia which are included in the kit during most investigations. In most cases, the equipment required can be carried in a standard camera case. The failure kit should be kept in order, ready for use, so no time is wasted putting it together when the client calls.

Table 1. Tools for the "Failure Analysis Kit"

35 mm Camera	Scalpel & Blades
28 mm Wide Angle Lens	Forceps
Camera Flash	Soft Brush
Tape Recorder	Wire Brush
Flash Light	Scribe
Magnifying Glass	Magnet
Measuring Tape	Mirror
Machinists Scale	Metal Markers
OD & ID Calipers	Sample Bags
Vernier Caliper	Labels
Micrometers	Replication Materials
Thread & Feeler Gauges	Dental Impression Material
Gloves	Krylon Spray
Wire & String	Basic Mechanic's Tools
Pencils & Pens	Solvent

LABORATORY EXAMINATION

The laboratory examination could easily be the subject of
a separate paper(s). As one might expect, the work done in
the laboratory, in conjunction with any particular failure
analysis investigation, is a function of the system or component under investigation, the suspected nature of the failure, and the condition of the part or component when received
in the laboratory. A partial list of types of testing which
might be done during a laboratory examination are listed in
the Appendix. As in the field investigation, documentation
of the testing conducted is of primary importance. Things
which might be considered obvious at the time of the examination may not be so in the future. Therefore, it is best to
record all testing methods, pertinent observations, and test
results in detail for future reference.

TESTING AND ANALYSIS

At the conclusion of the laboratory examination, various
hypotheses regarding the failure and incident will have been
formed. These hypotheses must be consistent with the background information obtained, the observations made in the
field and the results of the laboratory examination. The
various possible scenarios should then be subjected to scru-
tiny using exemplar testing and engineering analyses.

The exemplar test is a very useful method for establish-
ing the validity of conclusions developed as the investigation
progressed. Basically, an exemplar test is an attempt to
duplicate, in the laboratory, the observed field failure using
a system or component of the same or similar design to the one
which failed in the field. For example, suppose stress corrosion cracking has been proposed as a possible hypothesis for
the failure of a high strength fastener. The stresses acting
on the fastener and the environment in which the fastener was
operating should be known from information gained during the
initial portion of the investigation. Therefore, an exemplar
test using a similar fastener subjected to similar stresses
under a similar environment can be conducted in the laboratory
to determine if stress corrosion is a viable explanation for
the failure. The macro and micro appearance of the fracture
developed in the exemplar test can be compared to the actual
failed component to see if they are similar.

In the interest of time, the conditions used during the
laboratory exemplar test may be altered from those in the
field. For example, the temperature of the environment may

be increased, the environment may be more aggressive, or the stress may be increased to produce a failure in a reasonable period of time. However, if such accelerated testing is employed it must be justified and shown not to change the system behavior. This can be done either by subsequent long term testing or reference to information available in the literature.

The open literature can be a valuable tool in further developing or eliminating possible hypotheses relative to a failure. Thus, a well documented and organized technical library is extremely valuable, whether it be for a consultant, a central engineering office, or a large corporation. The key to a useful library is a filing index which allows for organization, retrievability, easy addition of new materials, and easy maintenance.

Engineers typically send for articles, subscribe to technical journals, collect data and reports, and are given data sheets by suppliers. This material, which may be useful on future projects, typically is buried in a project file or stacked on some shelf. If this material can be properly organized, with time, a useful library which becomes an invaluable resource in the solution to failure analyses can be built. The library may include codes, standards, catalogs, text books, technical articles, and other bookshelf materials.

One such index, based on a numerical coding system, was established and used by a metal producer. Each file has a number and a caption which describes that particular file. For example, the petroleum industry is indexed thusly:

    100:   Petroleum Industry
    100.1: Oil and Gas Production
    100.2: Petroleum Refining
    100.3: Petrochemical Processes

Petroleum Refining, 100.2, could be broken down into:

        100.2.1: Refining Processes
        100.2.2: Refining Equipment
        100.2.3: Refining Metallurgy

As the file folder grows and becomes bulky or too full of information for easy search, the subject can be broken down into logical subclassifications. In this way the system allows for easy expansion. The overall index can be organized to best suit the functions of the particular organization and should be put into a loose-leaf binder for easy revision and expansion.

Figure 1 is a flow chart showing how this system functions. Each engineer or technician who uses the library has, at his desk, a copy of the index. As an engineer comes across technical articles, data sheets, or other useful material, the appropriate index number, e.g., 100.2.3, is written on the first page. The purpose of the numbering system is to save time in writing titles longhand each time an article is indexed. The index number should be affixed immediately on incoming materials by the engineer. Books and shelf items can be indexed in the file folders by photocopying the cover or title page. The material is then given to a secretary or clerk for filing. If a journal is reviewed the appropriate articles can be indexed by the engineer and the whole journal can be given to the secretary who strips the necessary material for subsequent filing.

When an engineer needs information on a given subject, he or she refers to the index to get the appropriate file number(s) and then removes the material for review or duplication. When finished the file is returned to the secretary or clerk for refiling.

EVALUATIONS AND CONCLUSIONS

Only after obtaining all the background information available, and completing all testing and analyses, is the failure analyst in a position to make the necessary evaluations, form conclusions, and propose recommendations. During this process, the analyst must consider the reliability of the data obtained (for example, one would tend to put more credence in the results of a laboratory test than a witness statement). All alternate hypotheses consistent with the facts, evidence, and with engineering and physical principles should be considered before forming the final conclusions. The proper engineering principles and good scientific practice are then used to eliminate as many of the alternate hypotheses as possible. Any models or assumptions used to develop hypotheses and conclusions must be examined for their applicability and plausibility. The analyst must be prepared to substantiate the final conclusions, recommendations, and judgment criteria used in their development.

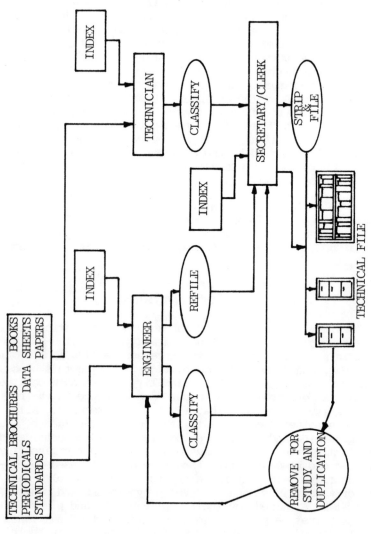

Figure 1. Flow Chart Showing Technical File Organization and Use.

CONCLUSIONS

Failure analysis is an engineering discipline which has developed as the complexity of technology and cost of failures have increased. In performing a failure analysis, the analyst must carefully define the problem using all background information, examinations, testing and analyses which are available or can be justified considering the economic ramifications of the failure. As discussed, all work should be properly documented as it is done, so no unanswerable questions regarding the results can arise in the future. Exemplar tests should be conducted where possible to justify hypotheses formulated during the investigation. A well organized technical library, where information on a specific subject can be easily located, is a tremendous asset. A simple method for developing such a library which can be used by organizations large and small has been described. Most importantly, the conclusions and recommendations developed during the analysis must be consistent with the facts and must be developed using good scientific practice. If these methods are followed, and the recommendations developed from the analysis are instigated, the probability of a similar failure recurring in the future should be greatly reduced.

REFERENCES

(1) R.A. Collacott, Mechanical Fault Diagnosis, Chapman and Hall, London, 1977.

(2) G.E. Moller, "Some Practical Aspects in the Investigation of Materials Problems," presented at the Energy Conference and Exhibition, Houston, Texas, Nov. 5-9, 1978, sponsored by the American Society for Mechanical Engineers.

(3) "Failure Analysis and Prevention," Metals Handbook, 8th Edition, Volume 10, American Society for Metals, 1975.

(4) R.W. Hertzberg, Deformation and Fracture Mechanics of Engineering Materials, John Wiley and Sons, 1976, Chapter 14, p. 543.

(5) V.J. Colangelo and F.A. Heiser, Analysis of Metallurgical Failures, John Wiley and Sons, 1974, Chapter 1, p. 1.

(6) Case Histories in Failure Analysis, American Society for Metals, 1979.

(7) Source Book in Failure Analysis, American Society for Metals, 1974.

(8) G.P. Coker, "Metallurgical Failure Analysis in the Petroleum Industry," presented at Corrosion '80, Chicago, Illinois, sponsored by the National Association of Corrosion Engineers.

APPENDIX A

OUTLINE OF BASIC FAILURE ANALYSIS METHODOLOGY

I. Problem Definition - become involved in the investigation
    as soon as possible after the incident.
    A. Incident Background
        1. Time and location
        2. Monitoring equipment read outs and operating logs.
        3. Witness statements
        4. History of subject system and critical compo-
            nent(s) - equipment records, operating conditions,
            maintenance and modifications.
        5. Agency reports - FAA, NTSB, OSHA, etc.
        6. Photographs
        7. Physical damage
    B. Engineering Design Background - How System or Compo-
        nent Functions
        1. System specifications
        2. Sales literature
        3. Assembly instructions
        4. Maintenance procedures
        5. Design specifications
        6. Design drawings - blueprints
        7. Fabrication and quality control procedures
        8. Engineering design analysis and reports
        9. Qualification test reports
       10. Relevant codes and standards.
       11. Service history of system or critical component(s)
            as a class.
    C. Legal Action Background
        1. Complaint
        2. Pleadings
        3. Interrogatories
        4. Affidavits
        5. Depositions
        6. Expert reports

II. Field Investigation - only possible if involved shortly
    after accident - have failure analysis kit ready for use.
    A. Wreckage Distribution and Documentation
    B. Component Damage, Distortions and Documentation
    C. Photographs and Documentation
    D. Mechanical Analysis and Documentation
    E. Fracture Analysis and Documentation
    F. Interviews with Witnesses, Plant Personnel, or Others
        Who Can Supply Useful Information
    G. Sample Selection for Further Laboratory Work

III. Laboratory Examination – every step should be well documented for future reference.
    A. Bench Testing
    B. Disassembly and Documentation
    C. Dimensional Check with Design Drawings
    D. Non-Destructive Inspection
    E. Visual Examination
    F. Examination Using Optical (<100X) Magnification
    G. Sample Cleaning and Preparation
    H. Scanning Electron Microscope Examination
    I. Energy Dispersive X-Ray Analysis
    J. Microprobe X-Ray Analysis
    K. Physical Properties
       1. Metallography
       2. Chemistry
       3. X-Ray Diffraction
    L. Mechanical Properties
       1. Hardness
       2. Strength
       3. Toughness

IV. Testing and Analysis
    A. Exemplar Tests
    B. Design Review
    C. Stress/Strength/Life Analysis
    D. Detectability Analysis – Quality Control
    E. Human Factors – Man/Machine Interaction, etc.
    F. Human Performance – Body Fatigue, etc.
    G. Probabilistic (Risk) Analysis
    H. Literature Review

V. Evaluation, Conclusions and Recommendations
    A. Explore Alternate Hypotheses
       1. Be consistent with the facts
       2. Be consistent with engineering and physical principles
       3. Consider data reliability
    B. Explain Technical Hypothesis and Conclusions
       1. Describe and justify assumptions
       2. Describe and justify engineering models
       3. Explain judgement criteria
    C. Propose Recommendations
       1. Be realistic – consider costs and feasibility
       2. Explain and justify recommendations

FAILURE OF A STEEL POT USED
FOR MELTING MAGNESIUM ALLOYS

Lawrence J. Kashar

Director, Metallurgical Services
Scanning Electron Analysis Laboratories, Inc.
Los Angeles, CA 90066

ABSTRACT

A steel pot used as crucible in a magnesium alloy foundry developed a leak that resulted in a fire and caused extensive damage. Hypotheses as to the cause of the leak included a defect in the pot, overuse, overheating and poor foundry practices.

Scanning electron microscopy, transmission electron microscopy, optical microscopy, and x-ray microanalysis in conjunction with dimensional analysis, phase diagrams and thermodynamics considerations were employed to evaluate the various hypotheses.

INTRODUCTION

A steel pot used to hold molten magnesium alloys leaked, Figure 1, releasing about 80 lbs. of molten metal onto the foundry floor. The resulting fire caused extensive damage, but, fortunately, no injuries. After the fire, the hole at the bottom of the pot was irregular and several inches across; the hole appeared to have been increased in size by erosion by molten magnesium and ensuing fire, Figures 2 and 3, no evidence of the original leaking hole remaining for analysis.

The pot was constructed by forming a hemispherical dome from plate and welding the dome to a cylinder. There is one vertical weld forming the cylinder. The material used is hot-rolled plain carbon steel, such as A.I.S.I. 1020 or 1022. As measured on a sample pot, the thickness averaged 0.366 inch.

131

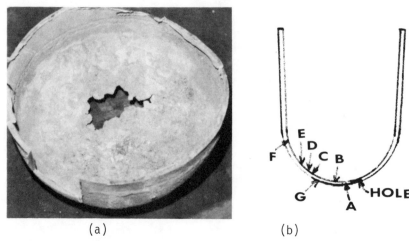

(a)

Figure 1a. The lower portion (dome and weld) of the failed pot showing the hole and the appearance of the inside surface. About 0.2X.

(b)

Figure 1b. Schematic cross-section of failed pot showing areas from which samples were taken.

Figure 2. Outer surface of pot adjacent to hole showing a highly eroded surface; 2.5X.

According to the foundry, the pots have a useful life of 70 to 100 heats; the failed pot had allegedly been used for approximately 30 heats. At the time of failure, the pot reportedly contained a rare-earth magnesium alloy, and was being held at 1460F in an open-top cylindrical fire-brick furnace. A natural gas burner utilizing a forced air blower was used to heat the furnace and pot. The burner flame was directed circumferentially around the inside of the furnace at about the same elevation as the dome/cylinder weld on the pot.

RESULTS OF EXAMINATION

Appearance of Pot

The failed pot was heavily oxidized to a brownish rust color. The hole in the pot was irregularly shaped, eccentric from the center of the dome, in a slightly bulged area and surrounded by steel about 0.06 inch thick. The thickness of the upper portion of the pot was approximately 1/4 inch. The edge of the hole was oxidized and eroded and showed evidence of local melting, Figure 3.

The thickness of the pot changed from about 0.1 inch to 0.2 inch or more in only about one inch (from C to E in Figure 16).

Microstructure of the Failed Pot

Around the perimeter of the hole the steel exhibited a very unusual set of microstructural bands, Figures 4, 5, and 8. Based on the appearance and on energy-dispersive x-ray (EDX) microprobe spectra, Figures 6 and 8, and on the wave-length spectrometer analysis of oxygen, Figure 7, the following areas (starting from the inside surface) were identified:

a. An aluminum-iron oxide scale or dross (area 1 in Figure 5).
b. An aluminum-magnesium-iron oxide constituent penetrating along grain boundaries (area 6).
c. A carbide-free iron-aluminum alloy layer (area 2).
d. Several rows of small aluminum-rich precipitate particles (arrow 3).
e. A carbon-enriched ferrite-pearlite layer, at some points reaching eutectoid composition (area 4).
f. An iron oxide outer layer (area 5).

Figure 3. Edge view of the hole through the pot (inside
surface at top) showing evidence of oxidation
and local melting; 88X.

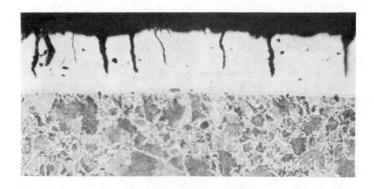

Figure 4. Cross-section showing the microstructure of the
inside surface of the pot at B in Figure 1b, note
the nearly eutectoid appearing area below the
completely carbide free area, nital etch; 54X.

Figure 5.

SEM of a cross-section of a sample adjacent to the hole (such as A in Figure 1b); unetched. EDX microprobe spectra were obtained at the numbered locations; 100X.

Figure 6.

X-ray map showing the distribution of aluminum in the area illustrated in Figure 5; 100X.

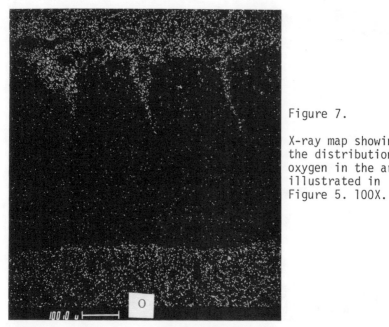

Figure 7.

X-ray map showing the distribution of oxygen in the area illustrated in Figure 5. 100X.

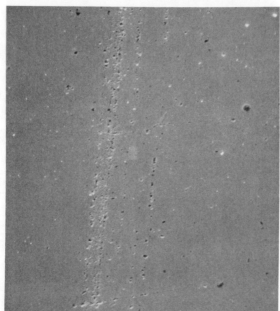

Figure 8.

Details of the rows of aluminum-rich precipitate particles shown at Arrow 3 in Figure 5; 600X.

A few inches from the hole, the thickness of the pot changed radically in a very short distance: from 0.1 inches at C to more than 0.2 inches at E (C and E are about one inch apart and represent points on an axisymmetric ring in which this thickness change occurred around the dome. The microstructure of the steel also varied between point C and E.

At D, midway between C and E, microstructure of the pot was a ferrite-pearlite mixture that was intermixed banded and large equiaxed ferrite and pearlite, Figure 9b. The outer surface of the pot at D intersected the banding, indicating that the erosion of metal responsible for the rapid change in cross-section had occurred from the outside surface, Figure 9a. The inner surface at D showed a thin carbide-free aluminum diffusion layer, Figure 9c.

The center of the pot thickness at E showed greater evidence of banding than did area D, Figure 9D. Further removed from the hole, at F, near the weld, the structure was completely banded, Figure 9e.

Pearlite Lamellae Structure

To examine the details of the pearlite structure, replicas were made at areas C and E and examined in a transmission electron microscope, Figures 10 and 11. In area C, all of the pearlite patches were composed of long carbide platelets, freshly formed from austenite with no apparent subsequent exposure to heat. In area E, some of the pearlite appeared to be freshly formed, whereas other pearlite patches contained short, spheroidal carbides, indicative of incomplete dissolution of carbide lamellae. This would occur if the temperature was not sufficient for complete austenitization.

Microstructure of Heat Treated Steel Samples

Using an unused melting pot as a source of sample material, pieces of steel were heated for one hour at various temperatures and air cooled to room temperature. This heat treatment simulated the temperature cycle that a pot might experience during one useage. The microstructure of the samples were examined in the unused and the heat treated conditions, Figures 12a through 12d.

The original microstructure was that of hot-rolled, banded ferrite-pearlite, Figure 12a; heating at 1450F did

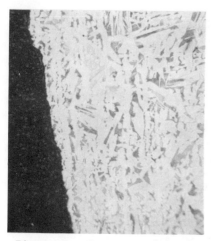

Figure 9a. Cross-section of
pot outer surface in area D
showing intersection of surface with banded structure,
indicating loss of material
from outer surface, nital
etch; 63X.

Figure 9b. Center portion of
pot cross-section in area D
showing that the banded structure of the hot rolled steel
has been partially eliminated
by subsequent heating; nital
etch; 63X.

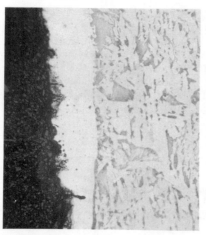

Figure 9c. The inner surface
of the pot cross-section in
area D showing the carbide-
free aluminum diffusion layer,
nital etch; 63X.

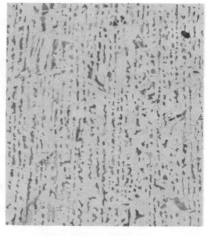

Figure d. Center portion of
pot cross-section in area E
showing the initial stages of
the homogenization of the
banding; nital etch; 63X.

Figure 9e. Center portion of pot cross-section in area F showing unaffected banded microstructure; nital etch; 63X.

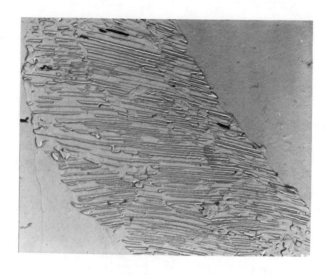

Figure 10. TEM replica of the ferrite/pearlite structure at C in Figure 1b showing fresh pearlite lamellae; picral etch; 4400X.

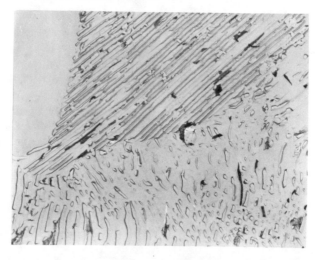

Figure 11. TEM replica of ferrite/pearlite structure at D in Figure 1b showing both fresh pearlite lamellae and partially dissolved pearlite lamellae, picral etch; 4400X.

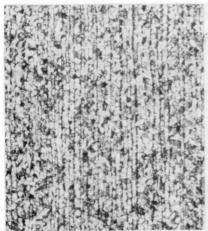

Figure 12a. Microstructure of an as-received unused melting pot; nital etch; 100X.

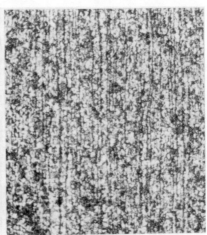

Figure 12b. Same as Figure 12a except heated for 1 hour at 1450F and air cooled; little or no apparent change, nital etch; 100X.

Figure 12c. Same as Figure 12a except heated for 1 hour 1650F and air cooled; most of the evidence of ferrite/ pearlite band has been eliminated; nital etch; 100X.

Figure 12d. Same as Figure 12a except heated for 1 hour at 1850F and air cooled;only traces of banding is still evident; nital etch; 100X.

not noticeably change this microstructure, Figure 12b.
Heating at 1650F for one hour eliminated about one-half of
the banding, Figure 12c; whereas heating at 1850F eliminated
all but some traces of the banding, Figure 12d.

Large Inclusion in Steel

A large mass of inclusions, extending through almost
one-half the remaining thickness of the pot, was found in a
sample removed from the area located at G, Figure 13. The
mass of inclusions included several large, irregularly
shaped particles and many small particles, Figure 14. Using
a wavelength spectrometer, all of these particles were found
to be oxides, Figures 15 and 16. Energy-dispersive x-ray
(EDX) spectra obtained from various areas of the inclusion
particles and the matrix steel showed that although iron
was the major element in all areas, it was more highly
concentrated in the steel than in the inclusions. Traces of
manganese and silicon were also present in all areas.

DISCUSSION

Along the inner surface of the pot, a thin iron-
aluminum layer was found, indicating that aluminum containing alloys had been melted in this pot. The diffusion of
aluminum into the steel apparently increased the chemical
potential of carbon in iron to the extent that it was swept
ahead of the aluminum alloy zone. The interface between
the iron-aluminum alloy and the carbon-enriched steel was
marked by rows of fine aluminum-rich precipitate particles,
probably aluminum carbide or aluminum nitride.

The iron-aluminum layer was composed of large grains,
the grain boundaries of which were oriented perpendicularly
to the inner surface of the pot. These grain boundaries
were found to be readily attacked by the melting slag or
dross.

Based on the variations found in the pearlite microstructures of the failed melting pot and comparing these
with the laboratory treated samples, the steel pot reached
a temperature of about 1650F at point D, between 1450 and
1650 at point E, and about 1450F at point F.

The carbide structure at point C was that of freshly
formed pearlite, whereas at E, both freshly formed and
spheroidized pearlitic lamellae were found. The speroidized

Figure 13.

Cross-section of the pot in area G in Figure 1b showing a large reddish inclusion in the steel; about 8X.

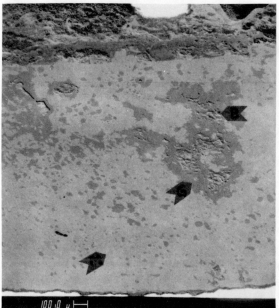

Figure 14.

SEM of inclusion area shown in Figure 13, arrows denote locations analyzed with an EDX microprobe; 40X.

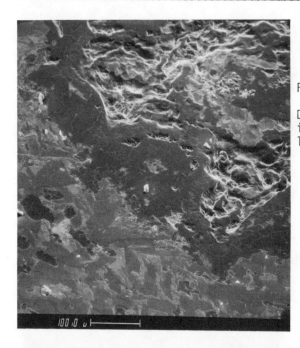

Figure 15.

Detail of area G
in Figure 14,
150X.

Figure 16.

X-ray map of the
distribution of
oxygen (obtained by
wavelength spectro-
meter) in the area
covered by Figure
15 showing that
the inclusion
particles contain a
lot of oxygen; 150X.

pearlite lamellae resulted from the incomplete dissolution of a pearlite colony during the final heating cycle of the pot, whereas, in the fresh pearlite areas, the temperature during the last heating cycle (fire) had been sufficient to completely austenitize the microstructure and therefore form fresh pearlite during cooling.

The variations in microstructure therefore indicate that the temperatures reached during the last melting cycle and ensuing fire varied by at least 200F in a very short distance on the pot. The highest temperatures were experienced close to the bottom of the pot and lower maximum temperatures were achieved at points along the side walls of the pot. The erosion of the pot was most severe at the bottom of the pot and had occurred by loss of material from the outer surface of the pot.

The appearance and the chemical analysis of the large mass of inclusions found in one area of the pot indicate that they were iron oxides particles. The source of these inclusions is subject to some question; potential sources include:

1. Present in the steel from the ingot as a result of the steelmaking practice.
2. Introduced into the pot in some repair sequence.

The examination of the pot did not find all of the characteristics that would be expected with either of these sources: 1) because the steel is formed from rolled sheet, if the oxide is from the ingot, it would be expected to be rolled out longitudinally or 2) if the oxide was introduced by weld repair, evidence of melting and HAZ would be present in the area. No evidence of melting or welding was observed in the area and the inclusion mass was not rolled out longitudinally in the cross-section examined (but could have been in the orthogonal section).

Based on all the evidence it is believed that the oxide mass was introduced in the steelmaking process. This thesis would predict that more than one oxide mass might have been present in the steel and that one of these other oxide masses had been present in the hole area and had caused the failure of the pot.

The presence of a large oxide defect in the steel could cause the pot to fail in the following manner: wear or erosion of the inner surface of the pot permitting the molten magnesium alloy to contact the iron oxide causing a thermite-like reaction, which by its strongly exothermic nature would locally melt the steel causing the leak. The ensuing fire in the furnace hearth would overheat the outside surface of the pot bottom in a very unstable manner resulting in its rapid erosion and unusual microstructure.

CONCLUSION

The failure of the steel pot used to hold molten magnesium alloys before casting was probably caused by the presence of a large iron oxide inclusion mass in the steel as the result of deficient steelmaking practice.

CASE HISTORIES OF METALLURGICAL FAILURES IN ELECTRONICS INDUSTRY

Arun Kumar*
Manager, Metallurgical Services
Scanning Electron Analysis Laboratories, Inc.
Los Angeles, CA 90066

ABSTRACT

The role of metallurgists in the electronics industry
is being increasingly recognized. Due to a rapid continual
growth of the electronics industry and a trend towards
miniturization, challenging materials problems are encountered every day. However, an understanding of routine materials
and processing problems is also of utmost importance to
assist the electronics and electrical engineers in design-
ing and manufacturing components and devices for high
reliability applications. Some processing problems are very
subtle and reappear periodically during manufacturing.
Carefully monitored strict process controls usually solve
such problems. The intent of this paper is to describe a
few commonly encountered processing problems in the electronics industry. Examples of failures involving plating
adherence problems, open and short circuits at plated
through holes of printed circuit boards, and hydrogen
embrittlement of copper during brazing of a diode package
are described.

PLATING ADHERENCE PROBLEMS

Electroless Nickel Plating Separation From Copper Alloy CDA175 Clips

Retaining clips for printed circuit board modules
exhibited plating flaking when the modules were inserted

*Work performed at the Technology Support Division, Hughes
Aircraft Company, Culver City, California 90230

and removed. The retaining clips had 150 μin thick electro-less nickel underplating and 100 μin thick gold plating. When the printed circuit board modules were inserted in the clips, shear and/or tensile stresses were generated at the copper base alloy/nickel plating and nickel/gold plating interfaces, depending on the location of the clip. The clips with plating failures and some good clips were cross-section-ed and metallographically examined. The good clips did not reveal any plating anomalies, however, the failed clips revealed a black layer at the copper alloy/nickel plating interface, Figure 1. Examination of the clip area with flaked plating in a scanning electron microscope (SEM) and analysis using wavelength dispersive x-ray (WDX) analysis revealed the black layer to be copper oxide. Review of the heat treatment procedure of copper alloy 175 clips (prior to plating) indicated that the furnace atmosphere could have caused surface oxidation which was not cleaned properly prior to plating. The copper oxide layer reduced the adhesion of the nickel plating on the clips and stresses developed during the module insertion caused the flaking to occur at the oxidized copper surface.

Corrective actions for this problem included the use of reducing or inert atmosphere in the furnace during the heat treatment of the clips and cleaning the clips in a bright dip solution with a composition of 17% H_2SO_4, 17% HNO_3, and 66% H_2O (by volume) and double rinsing in deionized water, prior to the plating operations. The bright dip solution dissolves copper oxides preferentially and does not dissolve any significant amount of the copper alloy.

Electroless Nickel Plating Separation
From OFHC Copper Leads

The lead material of a diode package was oxygen-free high-conductivity (OFHC) copper and the leads had 50 μin thick electroless nickel underplating and 150 μin thick gold plating. Parallel cracks, perpendicular to the lead length, were observed with corrosion products/oxides in the crack. Some areas with flaked plating were also observed. SEM examination and EDX/WDX analyses showed the corrosion products to be oxides and chlorides of copper. Cross-section of the leads were metallographically prepared and revealed cracks in the plating with necked-down ends and excessive corrosion of copper under the cracked areas, as shown in Figure 2. Review of the testing and installation procedures for the diodes indicated that the leads were bent back and forth too many times during electrical testing

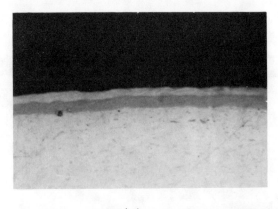

(a)   1000X

(b)   1000X

Figure 1. Electroless nickel underplating and gold
          plating on a copper alloy CDA175 module
          retaining clip. (a) shows a good plated
          clip and (b) shows a bad clip with copper
          oxide (black layer) at the copper/alloy
          nickel plating interface, where the
          separation occurred.

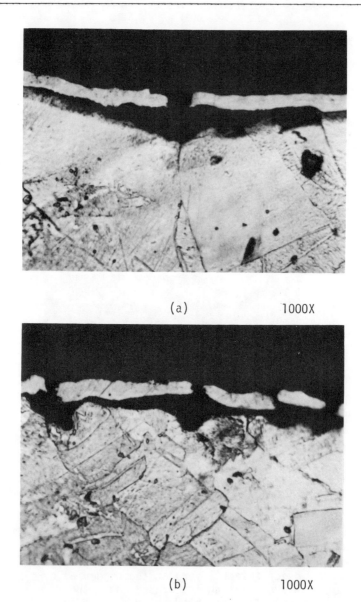

(a)   1000X

(b)   1000X

Figure 2. Cross-section of an OFHC copper diode lead with
          nickel underplating and gold plating. Plating
          cracked due to excessive back and forth bending
          of the lead, exposing the copper to oxidize,
          causing lead separation.

and installation. It was theorized that during bending of
the leads the hard electroless nickel underplating cracked
in a brittle manner and the gold plating cracked in a
ductile manner by necking down at the fractured ends. Some
underlying copper also formed a plastically deformed
groove at the cracked areas during the lead bending. After
installation of the diodes, plating cracks exposed the underlying copper forming oxides and chlorides. In some areas,
the corrosion process continued between cracks and separ-
ated the plating. Such a failure mechanism was duplicated
using laboratory exemplars of the diodes. It was concluded
that plating cracks and flaking were due to improper handling rather than a plating anomaly per se.

Tin Plating Separation From Copper Underplating On A Hybrid Package Lid

During electrical testing of a hybrid package it was
found that the output signals changed when the package was
gently tapped. The lid was cut from three sides and opened,
and spalled plating was found causing shorting or making
additional connections depending on their position in the
package, Figure 3(a). The lid material was Kovar with
copper underplating and tin final plating. The separation
had occurred between the tin plating and copper underplating. SEM examination and EDX/WDX analyses disclosed
the separation to occur at oxidized copper surface.
Cross-sections were examined for plating on the spalled
plating side as well as on the outside surface of the lid.
The inside surface revealed heavily oxidized copper below
the tin plating layer, Figure 3(b), while the outside
surface had relatively clean copper plating surface, Figure
3(c). A layering phenomenon was observed in the copper
underplating. Review of the plating procedures disclosed
a four-week delay between the copper plating and tin plating
steps. After copper plating, the lids were stacked up and
the top side of the top lid had most oxidation of copper
compared to the other side of the same lid, revealing the
observed anomaly. It was recommended that tin plating
should follow the copper underplating within 24 hours and
a cleaning step of bright dipping after copper plating be
performed.

(a)
1X

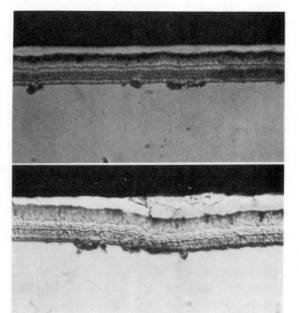

(b)
1000X

(c)
1000X

Figure 3. (a) Hybrid package with opened lid showing
spalled plating. (b) and (c) show the tin
plating over oxidized copper and clean copper,
respectively. Layering phenomenon can be seen
in the copper plating.

PRINTED CIRCUIT BOARD FAILURES
AT PLATED THROUGH HOLES

Open Circuit - Example 1

An open electrical circuit was found between the
plated through glass holes at U15-3 and U7-15 in a six-
layered printed circuit board after thermal cycling,
Figure 4(a). The art work of all the six layers was
reviewed and the paths connecting the two plated through
holes were traced. X-ray radiograph of the PCB was carefully examined and no anomalies were found in the conductor
traces connecting the two plated through holes. Cross-
sections were made through the plated through holes at
U15-3 and U7-15. The plated through hole at U7-15 was
normal, however, a discontinuity in the copper plating
was observed in the plated through hole at U15-3 causing
an electrically open circuit, Figures 4(a) and 4(b).
Localized thin or discontinuous copper plating in a
plated through hole was due to presence of contaminants or
air bubbles in the hole during the plating process. In the
present case, the copper plating was very thin in the failure area and did make an electrical contact during initial
testing. During thermal cycling, differential z-expansion
between the epoxy board and copper caused the thin plating
to crack.

Open Circuit - Example 2

During electrical testing of a four-layer circuit
board, an open electrical circuit was found between the
plated through holes at A and B, Figure 5(a). The art
work of all the layers was reviewed and the x-ray radiograph revealed continuous paths and no anomalies were
found in the conductors. Both plated through holes at A
and B were cross-sectioned and examined. The plated
through hole at A revealed an open between two layers
caused by a plating discontinuity, Figure 5(b), and the
plated through hole at B was normal. The plating discontinuity was caused by poor drilling using a dull drill
with improper speed and/or feed of the drill as was
observed by the non-uniform plating and nodule formation in
the plated layer.

Open Circuit - Example 3

An open electrical circuit was found in a six layer
printed circuit board between two adjacent plated through
holes at E7 and E8, Figure 6(a). Electrical continuity was

(a) 1X

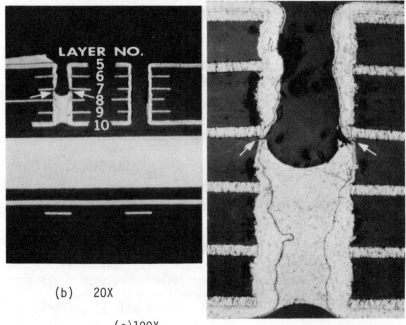

(b)   20X

(c)100X

Figure 4. (a) Optical photo of PCB showing the locations of
pads at U15-3 and U7-15; an electrical open was
found between these two pads. (b) Overall cross-
section showing the area of failure (arrows), and
(c) is a detailed view showing cracks in the thin
copper plating area.

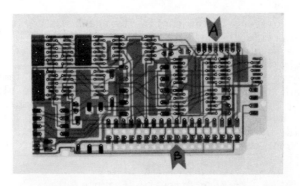

(a)   1X

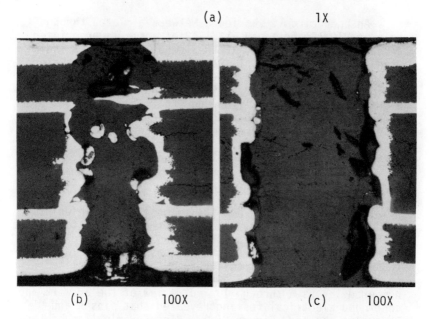

(b)   100X   (c)   100X

Figure 5. (a) x-ray radiograph showing the plated through
          holes at A and B; an open circuit was found
          between A and B. (b) and (c) are cross-sections
          of plated through holes at A and B, respectively.
          An open circuit can be seen at a plating void/
          discontinuity in (b).

found, however, if the continuity check was performed from
the back side of the PCB. A cross-section was made
through both adjacent plated through holes and a plating
void was found in the plated through hole at E7, as shown
in Figure 6(b). Detailed examination revealed some contaminant in the plated through hole causing the plating
void at E7, Figure 6(d), while the plated through hole at
E8 was normal, Figure 6(c). Since the plating void was on
one side of the conductor joining the two holes, continuity
was found when tested from one side of the board and lost
when tested from the other side.

Open Circuit - Example 4

An open circuit was found between a plated through
hole at U10-14 and a pad at J1-12 of a six layer printed
circuit board, Figure 7(a). Review of the artwork indicated that these two points were connected by a conductor
in layer 3. Examination of the conductor on an x-ray
radiograph revealed a break in the conductor at an
etching defect, Figures 7(b) and 7(c). The etching
defect could have been caused by either (a) a void in the
copper cladding, or (b) a contaminant on the copper prior
to the application of the photoresist, or (c) a contaminant
on the film, or (d) a pin hole in the photoresist.

Short Circuit

Short circuits are not too commonly found in printed
circuit boards, however, when a short circuit is found, the
analysis is quite difficult since two points could be
shorted through various electrical paths. A six layered
PCB revealed a short circuit between pin 39 and plated
through hole at U30-11, Figure 8. The six layers were
numbered layers 6 through 10 and review of the artwork and
continued electrical testing revealed that pins A and B
were also shorted, Figure 8(a). Close examination of the
x-ray radiograph revealed a conductor path shorting the
two pins, Figures 8(c) and 8(d). Therefore, the short
actually existed between pins A and B, which were
indirectly connected to pin 39 and plated through hole at
U30-11, respectively. The conductor shorting pins A and B
was formed by an etching defect which was due to either
insufficient development of the photoresist or improper
flushing of the residual photoresist leaving a copper area
which normally should have been etched away.

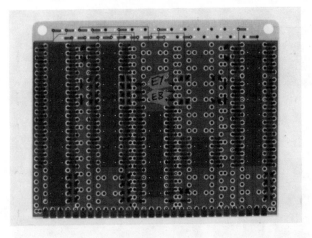

(a)   1X

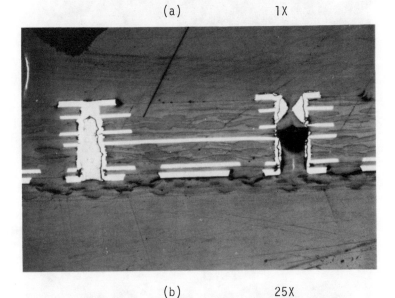

(b)   25X

Figure 6. (a) X-ray radiograph of a six layer PCB, which
had an open circuit between plated through holes
at E7 and E8. (b) Overall cross-section showing
the conductor connecting the plated through holes
at E7 and E8 and a plating void in the plated
through hole at E7.

(c) 100X

(d) 100X

Figure 6 (cont'd). (c) and (d) are detailed micrographs of plated through holes at E8 and E7, respectively. A plating void with contaminant entrapped in the plated through hole can be seen in (d).

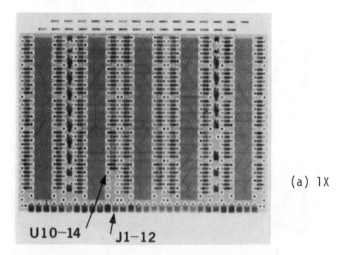

(a) 1X

U10-14   J1-12

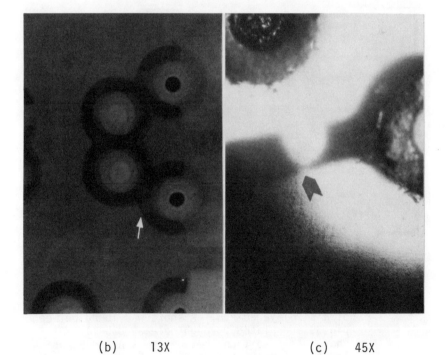

(b)   13X   (c)   45X

Figure 7. (a) Radiograph locating U10-14 and J1-12; an
electrical open was found between these two
points. (b) Enlargement of the radiograph
showing an etching defect (arrow). (c) is a
detailed optical photograph showing the etching
defect in the conductor.

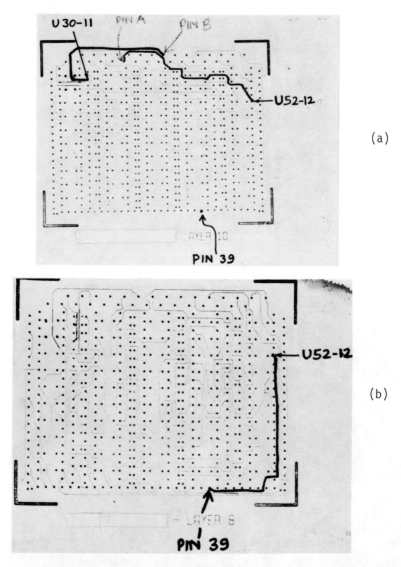

Figure 8. Artwork of (a) layer No. 10 and (b) layer No. 8
of a six layered PCB. A short was found between
pin 39 and plated through hole at U30-11. A
short was also found between pins A and B, which
led to determine the cause of shorting.

(c) 1X

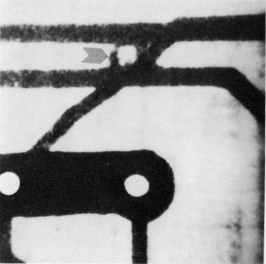

(d) 20X

Figure 8 (Cont'd). (c) Radiograph locating the area
between two conductors that were shorted. (d) is
a detailed view showing an additional conductor
piece causing the short (arrow).

HYDROGEN EMBRITTLEMENT OF A COPPER LEAD

Leads of a diode were supposed to be made from OFHC copper, however, they were made from copper containing high oxygen content. The leads had a nickel underplating, a gold final plating, and were brazed to the diode package in a hydrogen atmosphere. After brazing, the leads became embrittled and SEM examination of the fractured leads revealed voids and some oxidized areas surrounded by ductile fracture areas, Figure 9. Metallographic cross-section of the lead was examined optically and in the SEM and the micrographs are shown in Figure 10. Voids were observed as grain boundary networks and within the grains. Since the lead material had a much higher oxygen content than OFHC copper, the high oxygen in the form of cuprous oxide reacted with hydrogen during the brazing operation to form high pressure steam pockets. The following chemical reactions occurred:

$$2\ Cu\ +\ O \longrightarrow Cu_2O$$
$$Cu_2O\ +\ H_2 \longrightarrow 2\ Cu\ +\ H_2O$$

The high pressure steam pockets were observed as voids in the microstructure causing hydrogen embrittlement of the leads. The obvious corrective action in this case was to ensure that the lead material was OFHC copper.

ACKNOWLEDGEMENTS

The author is grateful to Dr. William G. Brammer, Jr. for his encouragement, to Mr. Ron Sapp for excellent metallography, and to Mr. Gerald L. Meldrum for the scanning electron microscopy.

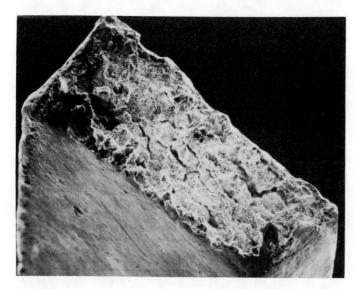

(a) 100X

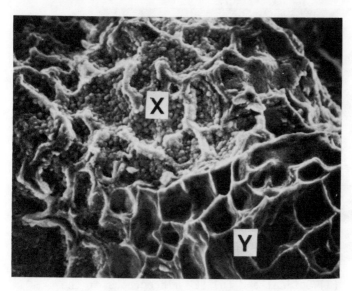

(b) 2000X

Figure 9. SEM micrographs of a hydrogen embrittled
copper lead fracture. (b) is a detailed micrograph of (a) and shows oxidized voids as X and
ductile fracture areas as Y.

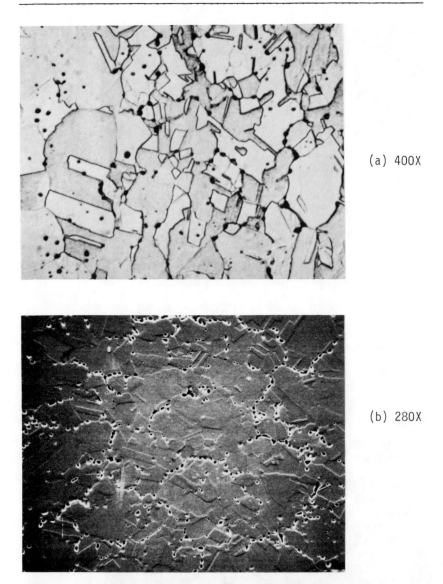

(a) 400X

(b) 280X

Figure 10. (a) Optical and (b) SEM micrographs of the
microstructure of the hydrogen embrittled
copper lead. Voids can be seen as grain-
boundary network and within the grains.

FAILURE ANALYSIS OF SILICA PHENOLIC NOZZLE LINERS

by
M. Katcher
The Marquardt Company

I. INTRODUCTION

This report describes The Marquardt Company's failure
investigation of cracking in two silica phenolic nozzle
liners while being subjected to proof testing. The proof
testing consisted of pressuring the nozzles to 14.1MPa
(2050psia) for 5 to 20 seconds. This failure investigation
describes the test articles exposed to proof testing,
defines the procedures employed in materials and test evaluation and presents a detailed solution by way of modifications to existing materials and process specifications.

Thirteen previously manufactured nozzle liners had been
subjected to proof-testing without experiencing cracking.
Therefore, a failure investigation team was organized which
detailed potential causes and established numerous action
items. Effective corrective actions were implemented
through changes in materials and process specifications in
cooperation with the affected vendors.

It was concluded that the cracks in the silica phenolic
nozzle liners were the result of the inadvertent substi-
tution of low strength fiber/fabric material that was used
in the manufacture of tape and later used to fabricate
silica phenolic liners. The low strength fiber/fabric was
not amenable to detection by the then current quality control procedures for assessing tape tensile properties. At
that time, the vendors tested the tape properties in the
warp as opposed to the bias direction. Hoop stresses on the
nozzles introduced during proof testing applied significant
bias direction loading. In testing after the failures, the
nozzles exhibited reduced mechanical properties including
tension and compression in the bias direction as compared to
nozzles which passed proof tests. Warp direction mechanical
properties could not be used to predict pass or fail in a
proof test.

II. NOZZLE INSULATION HISTORY IN PROOF TESTING

The convergent sections of two silica phenolic nozzle liners failed during proof pressure tests. The proof testing was conducted in Marquardt Jet Laboratory Test Cell No. 3 in Van Nuys, CA. in accordance with previously successful procedures. The combustion chamber assembly proof pressure testing is conducted upon completion of the manufacturing operations.

A. Proof Test

The proof testing consisted of pressurizing the nozzle assemblies to 14.1MPa(2050psia) for 5 to 20 seconds in accor-

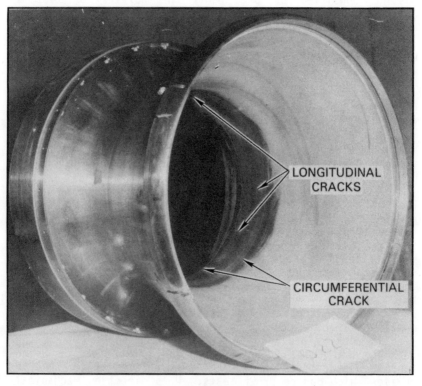

Fig. 1. Exhaust Nozzle With Insulator S/N 014R.

dance with Marquardt test specification. Nozzle S/N 014R
experienced its failure at 14.1MPa(2050psia) when a crack-
like noise was heard during the 344.0kPaa(50psia) post test
leak check. Leaks during proof test appear to have gone
through the longitudinal cracks in the throat insulation.
Note the longitudinal cracks indicated on Figure 1. It is
apparent that high pressure gas passed under an O-ring
through these cracks. Nozzle S/N 018 passed the proof and
leak tests but its silica phenolic nozzle liner also
cracked. A crack like noise was heard as the pressure
dropped between 9.7MPa(1.4ksi) and 7.6MPa(1.1ksi). Two
cracks located in the throat extended 360° around and
generally parallel each other.

B. Post Test Evaluation

Upon disassembly, the silica phenolic nozzle liner S/N
014R exhibited two(2) circumferential cracks upstream of the
nozzle throat and one(1) circumferential crack downstream of
the nozzle throat. At least six(6) longitudinal cracks connected the circumferential cracks and permitted leakage.
The cracks are plainly visible in Figure 1 which presents a
view looking forward from the aft end of the nozzle. Arrows
are used to emphasize the cracks. Only three of the six
longitudinal cracks are visible.

Careful but extensive efforts were applied to remove the
convergent insulation from the nozzle shells. The process
was made difficult by the excellent EPON 934 bonds between
the MXSE-55 and the MX-2646 convergent nozzle liner. Figure
2 shows reassembled pieces of the cut-off convergent liner
material. The dark patches indicate excellent adhesive bond
fracture surfaces produced during forced liner removal. The
light areas show different layers of MXSE-55; these failed
in preference to the bond. Two of the circumferential
cracks are plainly visible in the throat.

A view of the three circumferential cracks intersecting
the interior liner surface is presented in Figure 3. The
topmost crack occurred at a shear line defect about one inch
forward of the throat. The shear line defect was introduced
during tape wrapping by a split roller. The defect corresponded with the split in the roller.

A bond line separating the convergent and divergent

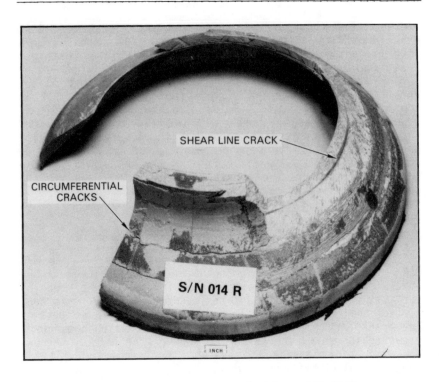

SHEAR LINE CRACK

CIRCUMFERENTIAL CRACKS

S/N 014 R

INCH

Fig. 2. Convergent Nozzle Liner S/N 014R.

liners may be seen at the left and right-hand cross-sections. The bond lines in liners S/N 014R and S/N 018 did not crack or separate. Since cracking occurred adjacent to the bond line in the convergent/throat section, it may be said that the EPON 934 bond is stronger than the inter-laminar strength of the MX-2646 silica phenolic laminate.

Post-test examination of Nozzle Liner Assembly S/N 018 revealed two circumferential cracks in the convergent phenolic liner, one approximately one inch forward of the throat and the other on the throat near the bond line. Both cracks extended 360° around the nozzle liner. No longi-tudinal cracks were found in nozzle liner S/N 018.

The facets on the shell/liner interface of S/N 018, confirm that an excellent EPON 934 bond existed between the liner and the MXSE-55 tape. This was also true for S/N 014R. The failure modes were cohesive within the EPON 934

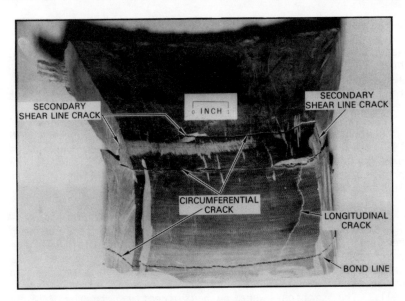

Fig. 3. Convergent Nozzle Insulator S/N 014R, Portions of Throat and Convergent Sections.

material itself.

Both nozzles were subsequently x-rayed at Armco Steel, using a 25 million volt Betatron machine. X-ray shots were taken every 30° around the circumference in a direction tangential to the nozzle surface. Two shots at each position covered both convergent and divergent sections. Unbonding was not observed between the nozzle liner, the MXSE-55 interlayer and the Inconel 718 nozzle shell. All circumferential cracks extended fully from the inner diameter of the nozzle liner to at least the MXSE-55 if not the Inconel 718 shell itself. The x-ray features of the crack disappear when near the liner MXSE-55/Inconel 718 interfaces.

C. Nozzle Insulation Manufacturing History

1. Proof Testing. Thirteen nozzles had been proof tested successfully on previous occasions to pressure conditions at least as severe as the proof pressure conditions imposed on Nozzle Assemblies S/N 014R and S/N 018. In no cases did the convergent nozzle liners fail.

2. <u>Nozzle Manufacturing History</u>. As testing progressed, changes were made to the basic method of liner manufacture and assembly to avoid cracking (delaminating), unbonds and shear lines. These changes responded to manufacturing problems and proof test results. Modifications were made to procedures when nozzle liners delaminated during proof test or during shipment or while shelved.

Unbonds were first discovered after Nozzle Assembly S/N 019R proof test. Further unbonds were found during subsequent x-ray of other nozzle assemblies. Shear lines in the throat were first discovered after failure of liner insulation from nozzles S/N 014R and 018.

The basic changes to the manufacturing methods and configurations were changes in molding technique and molding pressure. Two plies of MXSE-55 were first laid on the convergent and divergent sections of the Inconel 718 nozzle. Bias tape MX-2646 was then wrapped on a mandrel in two sections and then removed for placement in the nozzle shell. The sections were pushed directly onto the MXSE-55 from opposite ends of the nozzle and both composite materials were cured on the nozzle at 1.4MPa(200psi) pressure and 300°F temperature. Pressure was applied first and then temperature was allowed to rise slowly.

The method of manufacture was then changed in order to reduce potential residual stresses created during cure. It was felt that sensitivity to residual stresses could be avoided by curing the convergent liner on a separate mandrel rather than on the nozzle shell directly and subsequently, bonding the convergent liner to the nozzle. In this fashion, stresses locked into the liner at the 300°F cure temperature would be lower by reducing the length of the liner involved in the cure cycle. Also, the temperature and pressure were increased during cure in several stages rather than in one stage.

In the altered configuration the convergent liner insulator was wrapped on a mandrel separate from the nozzle and cured on the mandrel. The divergent liner insulator was wrapped on a mandrel and then machined to fit into the shell containing two layers of MXSE-55. The layers of MXSE-55 covered the inner surface of the nozzle shell. The divergent liner and the MXSE-55 were then cured on the nozzle shell as an assembly. The cured convergent liner was then room temperature bonded to the nozzle assembly using EPON 934 epoxy adhesive. The cure pressure and temperature for the convergent and divergent liners were 1.4MPa(200psi) and 300°F and were applied in staged operations. Precise machining of the cured convergent insulator and matching nozzle shell insures a good bond. Precise bond control was felt necessary to avoid space that might gather pressure. However, several nozzles made this way had bond joint separations as much as 0.080 inches.

As a result additional changes were made to the manufacturing techniques. The final configuration which failed during proof test is displayed in Figure 4. Fitup tolerances of .005-.010 inches between the convergent insulator and the MXSE-55 layer were imposed. X-ray films of subsequent nozzle assemblies and views of the dissected nozzle assemblies from Assemblies S/N 014R and 018 revealed excellent bond quality between the convergent liner and the MXSE-55. To insure that two complete layers of MXSE-55 would remain after fitup matching, a third layer of MXSE-55 was applied. Much of this layer was machined away to provide accurate contours.

The molding pressure was also increased to 6.3-6.9MPa (900-1000psi) from 1.4MPa(200psi) for both convergent and divergent liners. Literature data indicated that increasing molding pressure to 1000psi would improve composite strength and provide further insurance against insulation failure. These data were based on warp direction tests of tape properties which will be shown in later paragraphs to be misleading. Bias direction tests would have been more appropriate.

III. Failure Analysis Procedures and Results

A failure analysis team was assembled by Marquardt to investigate the cracks in the silica phenolic liners. This was the first time cracking had been observed in the convergent liners and immediate corrective action was required before production could continue. The failure analysis team recognized ten potential failure modes. The potential failure modes are as follows.

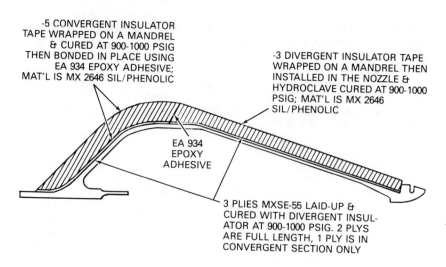

-5 CONVERGENT INSULATOR TAPE WRAPPED ON A MANDREL & CURED AT 900-1000 PSIG THEN BONDED IN PLACE USING EA 934 EPOXY ADHESIVE; MAT'L IS MX 2646 SIL/PHENOLIC

-3 DIVERGENT INSULATOR TAPE WRAPPED ON A MANDREL THEN INSTALLED IN THE NOZZLE & HYDROCLAVE CURED AT 900-1000 PSIG; MAT'L IS MX 2646 SIL/PHENOLIC

EA 934 EPOXY ADHESIVE

3 PLIES MXSE-55 LAID-UP & CURED WITH DIVERGENT INSULATOR AT 900-1000 PSIG. 2 PLYS ARE FULL LENGTH, 1 PLY IS IN CONVERGENT SECTION ONLY

Fig. 4. Nozzle Shell and Insulator Configuration.

Possible Causes of Failure

(1) Silica phenolic modulus of elasticity change due to cure pressure.
(2) Wrinkles and/or secondary shear lines.
(3) Moisture pickup by silica phenolic during hydroclave cure.
(4) Modification to the convergent mandrel.
(5) Deficient materials properties (phenolics).
(6) Deficient Inconel 718 properties.
(7) Nozzle/insulator structural design deficiency.
(8) Tape angle change.
(9) Deficiency introduced by process change(s) (new vs. old)
(10) Assembly process deficiency

Failures modes 1, 3, 4, 6 and 10 were discounted after thorough investigation and will not be discussed here. It was necessary to mention them for completeness. The investigation of the other potential failure modes are documented in the following paragraphs.

1. <u>Wrinkles and/or Secondary Shear Lines</u>. Wrinkles are

defined as a waviness in each laminate plane. They may be seen in cross-section when the view-line is parallel to the plane of laminations. Wrinkles may be considered for the purpose of discussion to look like a sine wave. Wrinkles are more detrimental when the nodes occur with greater frequency per unit length. A wrinkle may occur when excess matrix material such as phenolic accumulates in one region or when the end of one lamination is covered by another. It may also occur when pressure at the end of a laminate imposes buckling loads. Observation of the cross-section of the insulators similar to that shown in Figure 3, but polished for precise viewing, failed to detect wrinkles. However, another kind of defect was found and appears as a line in Figure 3. Actually this kind of defect is a secondary shear plane and lies generally parallel with the nozzle surface while cutting across the laminations. This type of defect was observed at several throat locations around the circumferences of both liners S/N 014R and S/N 018. At high magnification, the shear plane appears as a jog in each laminate plane.

One of the three circumferential cracks located in the Nozzle Assembly liner S/N 014R follows part of a shear plane and intersects the interior surface forward of the throat. No cracks in the liner S/N 018 follow the shear plane. Figure 3 shows two cross-sections of convergent insulation from liner S/N 014R. Note the secondary shear line crack. Because the crack follows the shear line it is detrimental and must be avoided. It indicates weakness.

To avoid such shear planes in the future, an investigation into the cause was made. A segmented roller applied pressure to the impregnated tape during wrapping. The position of the defect corresponds to a separation between rollers. Segmented rollers were used in order to adjust to the variation in speed between the inner diameter and the outer diameter of the tape being wrapped around the rotating mandrel. By slowing down the rotation speed of the mandrel, a solid roller can be used with equal success. This change in the roller was made and the problem was eliminated. However, to eliminate the potential for shear lines in future assemblies, the process specification was changed to assure they will not occur. An inspection procedure was also imposed. Cross sections will be cut and polished for viewing at four locations around the circumference of each insulator prolongation.

2. <u>Deficient Silica Phenolic Laminate Properties</u>. The properties of MX-2646 material were monitored by the Quality Control Department to determine if they met drawing requirements. Specific gravity (1.68-1.77), compression strength perpendicular to the laminate 379.2MPa(55.0ksi min.), acetone extraction (0.30% max.), and residual volatiles (0.70% max.) tests were performed to insure material integrity.

Table 1 presents a list of these average properties for all nozzle insulation used in this program. All previous insulation passed the above criteria. Additional data were also supplied to Marquardt and are shown under the columns entitled Tapes. After final machining, an alcohol penetrant test used was to inspect for defects and cracks.

If defective properties of the silica phenolic MX-2646 had caused the nozzle liners to crack, one might have deter-

Table 1. Average Properties of Proof Tested Tapes/Laminates.

		TAPES				LAMINATES			
		RESIN	VOLATILES	LAMINATE FLOW, %			COMP.	ACETONE	RESIDUAL
EXIT NOZZLE	LOT NO.	CONTENT %	CONTENT %	689.5 kPa (100 PSI)	1034.2 kPa (150 PSI)	SPECIFIC GRAVITY	STRENGTH MPa (KSI)	EXTRACTION %	VOLATILES %
S/N 001	T-108	21.6	3.9	0.2		1.75	441.3 (64.0)	0.20	0.57
007	T-108	21.6	3.9	0.2		1.73	437.8 (63.5)	0.13	0.50
024	T-484	21.3	3.5		0.6	1.76	435.1 (63.1)	0.24	0.64
014	A8-073 A8-099	21.4	3.5		0.5	1.75	434.4 (63.0)	0.28	0.60
020	T-484	21.3	3.5		0.6	1.77	426.8 (61.9)	0.26	0.62
009	T-108	21.0	3.8	0.2		1.74	420.6 (61.0)	0.20	0.50
008	T-108	21.0	3.8	0.2		1.74	415.8 (60.3)	0.10	0.50
016	T-484	21.3	3.5		0.6	1.76	430.1 (62.5)	0.28	0.60
015	T-484	20.9	3.4		0.7	1.75	410.9 (59.6)	0.20	0.60
019	A8-073	21.3	3.5		0.4	1.75	442.0 (64.1)	0.23	0.60
019R	A8-073	21.3	3.5		0.4	1.75	442.0 (64.1)	0.23	0.60
003	T-108	20.9	3.8	0.2		1.74	422.0 (61.2)	0.16	0.60
016R 027	A8-073	21.1	3.5		0.4	1.74	440.6 (63.9)	0.23	0.60
014R	A9-057	19.4	3.4		1.1	1.75	410.9 (59.6)	0.20	0.60
018	A9-057	19.6	3.4		1.0	1.74	400.6 (58.1)	0.20	0.57
N1000 BN200 BN1000	A9-113 A9-113 A9-113	20.4	4.2		1.0				

mined this immediately from the specified tests. However, the defective material met all drawing requirements and could not be distinguished from good material. Scanning the properties shown in Table 1 shows that differences do exist between the properties of Lot A9-057 and those of other lots of tape but, no particular significance could be attached to these small differences at this point in the investigation. Investigative efforts were therefore continued on other possible failure mode causes.

2.1 <u>Compression Strength Perpendicular to Laminates</u>. The compression strength of laminates made from Lot A9-057 used in convergent Nozzle Assemblies S/N 014R and S/N 018 had values below 413.7MPa(60.0ksi) whereas all other lots except one had higher values. Pursuing this anomaly, it was determined that the direction of applying the compression loads was perpendicular to the laminate plane. Half-inch diameter test coupons for these tests were removed from the forward test ring of each convergent insulator. Because only the phenolic binder was being squeezed, test data were only of limited value. The fabric added no support in this test and the fabric/binder bond underwent minimum stress. Differences in compression values from lot to lot were small. Successful and unsuccessful proof tests could not be distinguished in this manner. Compression strength in this direction was therefore not a good characteristic for rating and distinguishing poor quality material.

2.2 <u>Laminate Flow</u>. Certain other properties showed values that distinguished the results obtained from Nozzles S/N 014R from previously tested nozzles. These include the values for resin content and laminate flow. The failed nozzle insulators using Lot A9-057 were made from tapes whose resin content was uniquely under 20.0% and whose laminate flow was uniquely above 0.7% when compared to the average values for previously used lots. Bias tensile and compression test data shown in Tables 2 for Lot A9-057 material (liners S/N 014R and S/N 018) also showed values significantly below tests on other lots of material. It was therefore felt at the initial phases of the failure analysis, that a connection between these phenomena could exist. Laminate flow was eventually eliminated as a failure mode because Lot A9-113, which was used to make high strength insulators N1000, BN200 and BN1000, had the same laminate flow as Lot A9-057 used to make the cracked insulators. The laminate flow values could not be used to distinguish bad lots of impregnated tape.

2.3 <u>Resin Content</u>. Resin content was the second property that was lower in the cracked material relative to previous material. Also, Lot A9-141 which was used for production nozzles had an extremely low resin content, in fact lower than specification requirements (18-22%). However, bias tensile and compression strengths for this material per Table 3 significantly exceeded values obtained from the cracked insulators of chambers S/N 014R and S/N 018 shown in Table 2 and panel tests on lot A9-057 also in Table 3. Therefore, the effect of resin content variations within 18% to 22% was not considered to significantly effect laminate fracture characteristics.

2.4 <u>Fabric Properties</u>. The Marquardt Company sought a cause-effect relationship between the history of Lot A9-057 and nozzle insulater cracking. A change had been made by

Table 2. Average Bias Mechanical Properties from Insulators.

LOCATION	LAMINATE ANGLE DEGREE	TENSILE											
		S/N 019R		S/N 014R		S/N 018		N1000		BN200		BN1000	
		FTU*	E**	FTU	E	FTU	E	FTU	E	FTU	E	FTU	E
CONVERGENT	0	95.1 (13.8)	20.7 (3.0)			57.2 (8.3)	14.5 (2.1)			123.4 (17.9)	19.3 (2.8)	100.7 (14.6)	19.3 (2.8)
CONVERGENT	15	92.4 (13.4)	19.3 (2.8)	49.0 (7.1)	12.4 (1.8)	52.4 (7.6)	15.9 (2.3)			113.1 (16.4)	20.7 (3.0)	78.6 (11.4)	22.8 (3.3)
CONVERGENT	30	58.6 (8.5)	20.7 (3.0)										
THROAT	0			52.4 (7.6)	13.8 (2.0)	45.5 (6.6)	12.4 (1.8)	85.5 (12.4)	21.4 (3.1)	105.5 (15.3)	17.2 (2.5)	89.6 (13.0)	18.6 (2.7)
THROAT	45	38.6 (5.6)	17.2 (2.5)										
THROAT	60	35.2 (5.1)	17.2 (2.5)										
		COMPRESSION											
		FCU	E	FCU	E	FCU	E	FCU	E	FCU	E	FCU	E
CONVERGENT	0	262.7 (38.1)	17.9 (2.6)	180.6 (26.2)	15.2 (2.2)	163.4 (23.7)	13.1 (1.9)			251.7 (36.5)	15.9 (2.3)	244.8 (35.5)	17.2 (2.5)
CONVERGENT	15					95.8 (13.9)	11.0 (1.6)			210.3 (30.5)	13.1 (1.9)	239.9 (34.8)	14.5 (2.1)
THROAT	0					188.9 (27.4)	11.7 (1.7)	266.1 (38.1)	16.8 (2.4)	261.3 (37.9)	15.2 (2.2)	258.6 (37.5)	15.2 (2.2)
THROAT	15									237.2 (34.4)	13.8 (2.0)	208.2 (30.2)	15.2 (2.2)
THROAT	45					171.7 (24.9)	11.0 (1..6)						

* MPa (KSI)
** MPa x 10³ (KSI x 10³)

Table 3. Bias Panel Data on MX-2646.

LOT	A9-057	A9-113	A9-113	A9-141
Mold Pressure, MPa (psi)	34.5 (500)	34.5 (500)	13.8 (200)	13.8 (200)
Specific Gravity	1.74	1.76	1.70	1.72
Tensile Strength, MPa (ksi)	60.0 (8.7)	123.4 (17.9)	116.5 (16.9)	118.6 (17.2)
Tensile Modulus, 10^3 MPa (10^6 psi)	13.1 (1.9)	15.9 (2.3)	20.7 (3.0)	17.9 (2.6)
Tensile Elongation, %	0.7	2.6	1.0	1.5
Compression Strength, MPa (ksi)	—	—	196.5 (28.5)	197.3 (28.9)

the tape vendor in the manufacture of this lot when compared to other lots. The source of the fabric was temporarily changed. Lot A9-057 was used to make the insulators which subsequently cracked. Insulators using other lots of tape did not crack.

The original quality control procedures were unable to distinguish a cracking tendency between different lots of tape. Marquardt therefore revised its materials and process specifications by converting from warp direction to bias direction testing of fabric panels. Vendor panel data is shown in Table 3. Compared to lots processed after A9-057, the bias direction tensile strength of A9-057 is half the others. These tests were run at the tape manufacturer and corroborates the results on production insulators shown in Table 2. Lot A9-057 was used to make nozzles S/N 014R and 018; Lot A9-113 was used to make N1000, BN200 and BN1000. Lot A9-141 was used to make subsequent production nozzles and all of these passed proof testing without cracking.

As explained previously in paragraphs 2.1, 2.2, and 2.3, several potential sources of laminate defects were eliminated. The only source of laminate defect that cannot be rejected is the source of fabric for Lot A9-057. The convergent throat sections of nozzles from S/N 014R and S/N 018 were made from Lot A9-057 and were the only insulation to show significantly inferior bias strength properties. While it is as yet a mystery as to the cause of fiber/fabric defectiveness, it remains the only source of poor laminate quality that can be identified.

3. Nozzle Insulator Structural Design Deficiency. The
stress analysis of the nozzle and insulator performed by
Marquardt's stress group shows that liners S/N 014R and S/N
018 were stressed at or beyond the capability of their
materials. Several analytical assumptions were made. A
proof pressure of approximately 13.8MPa(2000psi) at which
the nozzle tends to expand .0419cm(0.0165inches) on the
radius of the throat was assumed. Also, a rigid bond between the insulation and the Inconel 718 nozzle shell was
assumed in the analysis. Additionally, warp direction properties were input to the computer program. To complement
the analysis, material properties were obtained in the hoop
direction, normal to the laminate and in interlaminar double
shear. If the predicted stresses exceeded the average
material properties, then failure was a distinct possibility.

The highest stress predicted was in the hoop direction.
This corresponded to a zero angle (bias direction) test.
Analysis showed these stresses to be in tension at 60.0MPa
(8.7ksi). Tensile data from cracked insulation of S/N 014R
and S/N 018 from Table 2 showed the average laminate
strength of the defective material to be marginal, in the
order of a 49.6MPa(7.2ksi) average. In fact, liner S/N 014R
cracked longitudinally indicating the presence of excessive
hoop stresses in relation to material strength.

The strength of the interlaminar bond is strong enough
to withstand crushing loads. Stress analysis showed the

Table 4. Average Interlaminar Bond Strengths, MPa(ksi).

LOCATION	S/N 019R	S/N 014R	S/N 018	N1000	BN200	BN1000
DOUBLE SHEAR						
Convergent		49.6 (7.2)	41.4 (6.0)		60.7 (8.8)	60.7 (8.8)
Throat	80.0 (11.6)		26.9 (3.9)	67.6 (9.8)		
BOND TENSILE						
Convergent					12.4 (1.8)	9.0 (1.3)
Throat	18.6 (2.7)			11.7 (1.7)		

stresses normal to the laminate at a point near the inner diameter to be in compression at 22.1MPa(3.2ksi). Compression strengths reported in Table 1 for cracked and uncracked nozzle liners are in excess of 399.9MPa(58.0ksi). This then could not have been the mode of failure. In fact, no evidence of crushing was found after proof testing and examining the fractures of liners S/N 014R and S/N 018.

Stress analysis predicts that the strengths of the interlaminar bond is not strong enough to withstand tension loads. Additional analysis of stresses normal to the laminate near a point on the liner outer diameter at a forward section of the throat showed values in tension as high as 33.1MPa(4.8ksi). This is more than double the capability of the material coupons. Values of bond strength developed during this program are presented in Table 4. Good material as represented by S/N 019R, or "BN200" can generate a bond strength of between 9.0MPa(1.3ksi) and 18.6MPa(2.7ksi). This indicates that a distinct potential mode of failure has thus been identified. Evidence of weak interlaminar bond strength is shown by the circumferential cracks in Figures 1, 2 and 3. Views of the throat cross-section show the circumferential cracks running parallel with the laminate angle.

Although the predicted tensile stresses exceed the bond strength of isolated material coupons, Marquardt is unable to conclude that a design deficiency exists because of weak interlaminar bonds. Thirteen nozzles manufactured with good materials had successfully passed proof testing confirming the designs adequacy. At present there are no plans for conducting the tests from which more definitive data on material/liner properties and liner-to-shell bond joints could be obtained. These would be needed to provide a precise definition of the tensile capabilities of the combined liner, bond and metal structure in the convergent section adjacent to the nozzle throat.

The interlaminar shear stress as developed by stress analysis for proof pressure was 13.1MPa(1.9ksi). Material tests were preformed in double shear to determine the interlaminar shear strength of cracked and uncracked liners. The values shown in Table 4 for cracked insulation S/N 014R and S/N 018 was 49.6MPa(7.2ksi) and 41.4MPa(6.0ksi) in the convergent section and 26.9MPa(3.9ksi) in the throat. These values exceed the 13.1MPa(1.9ksi) obtained by stress

analysis. Based on the relationship between material
properties and the calculated applied stress, interlaminar
shear cannot be considered a mode of failure. Also, no
evidence of cracking due to shear stresses in the plane of
the laminate were found.

Stress analysis showed the tensile stress in the plane of
the laminate in the throat to be 33.1MPa(4.8ksi). A tension
test in the zero degree direction simulates this kind of a
loading. Actual tests on the throat material from cracked
insulation in Table 2 showed low average values for liners
S/N 014R and S/N 018 of 52.4MPa(7.6ksi) and 45.5MPa(6.6ksi),
respectively. Applied tensile stresses in the laminate
plane of the insulator were therefore not a significant
factor in material failure.

In review, then, the primary stresses based on structural analysis and subscale testing which induced failure of
throat insulation were in the hoop direction and normal to
the interlaminar bond. Visual evidence of longitudinal and
circumferential cracks in liners S/N 014R and S/N 018 support these conclusions. No deficiency from a design standpoint is apparent.

4. Tape Angle Change A change in tape angle may result in
a low density area that provides a path of weakness. Extra
phenolic with a local absence of reinforcing fabric contri-
butes to this potential fracture path. A tape angle change
may be caused by a variation in roller pressure during tape
wrapping, the intermittent application of smaller width
tape, or variations in cure pressure across different sections. These events can lead to regions or planes of weakness.

Tape angle changes were not observed during the failure
investigation. The convergent insulators removed from
Nozzle Assemblies S/N 014R and S/N 018 had tape angles that
meet drawing requirements. In addition, low density areas
or foldovers were not observed at or near any of the fractures. The fractures followed single tape planes between
the inner diameter of the insulators and the Inconel 718
interface. Tape angle changes can be dismissed as a possible cause of failure on the subject silica phenolic liners.

5. Deficiency Introduced by Process Changes. Essentially
two major changes were made to initial procedures for manu-

facturing ASALM-PTV nozzle insulators. These were discussed
in detail in Section II, paragraph C2, but will be briefly
reviewed here. Initially, both the convergent and divergent
insulators were wrapped directly onto the ramjet nozzle as
one piece and cured at 1.4MPa(200psi). For the first change
the divergent insulator was wrapped on a separate mandrel
and cured directly on a nozzle while the convergent insulator was wrapped on a separate mandrel, cured, and then
bonded to the nozzle. For the second change the cure pressure was increased to 6.9MPa(1000psi) from 1.4MPa(200psi).
Also, a third layer of MXSE-55 was cured onto the convergent
nozzle prior to bonding the insulator. This procedure plus
tighter machining tolerances improved bond quality.

As a result of the convergent insulator failures of S/N
014R and S/N 018, a major question needed to be answered.
Did the manufacturing changes cause the cracks? In all
cases except for S/N 014R and S/N 018, convergent insulators
had not cracked because of poor material quality. The
increase in cure pressure can also be dispelled as a cause
for failure. Test data shown in Tables 2 and 3 indicate
that increased cure pressure reduces strength only slightly
and increases modulus slightly. It does not account for the
large strength and modulus reductions displayed by the two
cracked convergent insulators from nozzles S/N 014R and 018.

Better bond quality between the Inconel 718 shell and
silica phenolic insulator can also be dispelled as a cause
of insulator failure. An analysis of stress in the nozzle
insulator was performed by the Marquardt stress group using
warp direction properties. It was concluded that improving
bond quality from a "no bond" to a "rigid bond" condition
would reduce the hoop stress, the stress normal to the
laminate and the interlaminar shear stress. Only the tensile stress in the plane of the laminate would increase from
25.1MPa(2.8ksi) to 33.1MPa(4.8ksi). This increase is insignificant compared to the actual material strength of the
cracked insulation (nozzles S/N 014R and S/N 018). Average
tensile strengths from Table 2 were 52.4MPa(7.6ksi) and
45.5MPa(6.6ksi) respectively. Thus, improvements in bond
strength between the convergent insulator and the Inconel
718 nozzle did not contribute to the insulator failures.

The only change common to the insulators from nozzles
S/N 014R and S/N 018 and to no other nozzles was use of Lot
A9-057 material. Whenever this lot of material was strength

tested in the bias direction, the values were half those of
other lots in tension and 75% of other lots in compression.
This strength deficiency was not introduced by Marquardt
process changes but rather by procedures peculiar to the
tape vendor.

IV. QUALITY CONTROL CHANGES

A. Specifications

To insure against future material defects a new specification was imposed on the tape supplier and nozzle manufacturer which required them to meet bias direction strength
values for bias tape. These values were deemed necessary to
meet burst pressure conditions. The manufacturer was required to meet strength values by testing prolongations of
convergent liners for tension and compression strength;
minimum values of 90MPa(13.0ksi) and 228MPa(33.0ksi),
respectively, were specified. These prolongations are
forward and aft extensions of each convergent nozzle liner
made on the same mandrel, cured, and then cut off for test
coupon manufacture. They were also required to test incoming tapes to insure against deterioration during shipment.

Shear lines as previously discussed had been discovered
in the throat portion of the convergent liners. These defects were observed by cutting the liners radially and
observing a polished cross-section. Figure 3 shows a cross-
section of the insulation from the throat of chamber S/N
014R. The shear line is clearly indicated between the circumferential cracks. Fractures were noted along these shear
lines. Therefore, the manufacturing specification was up-
graded to require polished cross-sections of prolongations
and the rejection of assemblies with such shear lines.

B. Subsequent Insulation History

Ten(10) nozzle assemblies had been made to the above
procedures and ten(10) had been successfully proof tested at
the time that this report was prepared Tensile and compression testing of coupons cut from prolongations at both
ends of ten(10) silica phenolic exhaust nozzle liners have
been performed. A number of these tests yielded values as
much as 10% less than the minimum values specified 90 MPa

(13.0ksi) tenile and 228MPa(33.0ksi) compression. However, the Materials Engineering Department considered these results as normal variations that can occur when test coupons are removed from different sections of the convergent insulator. The strengths of the prolongations from which quality control tests coupons were removed may not yield the same values as are obtained from coupons removed from the useable sections of nozzle liners. The molding conditions of the prolongations may be slightly different from the molding conditions of the useable sections. Also, the strength values specified were chosen as a result of tests on the useable section of nozzles S/N 019R, "N1000", "BN200" and "BN1000" (Tales 2 and 3), and not on prolongations. The specified values were subsequently reduced 10% to the values reported in paragraph IV. A.

V. CONCLUSIONS AND RECOMMENDATIONS

Upon completion of the failure investigation into the potential failure modes of proof tested insulators, Marquardt concluded that the longitudinal cracking of the convergent exhaust nozzle insulators was due to the use of bad fiber/fabric material by a supplier. This material was used in the manufacture of silica phenolic tape that was later used by Marquardt's exhaust nozzle liner supplier. The bad fiber/fabric could not be distinguished by then current quality control procedures which assessed tape strength properties in the warp as opposed to the bias direction. It was also determined that the introduction of the bad fiber/fabric material was the only distinctive difference between the nozzle insulators that failed and other nozzles that had successfully passed. Therefore, Marquardt resumed manufacture of nozzle liners with controlled fiber/fabric materials and these have been successfully proof tested.